FREE Plan Rebate
See Page 247

FREE Material Take-Off
See Page 250

W9-BOT-754

LOWE'S HOME PLANS

SMALLER LOT
featuring apartment garage plans

LOWE'S LEGACY SERIES

Featuring smaller lot home plans
and apartment garage plans
from Lowe's Legacy Series.

Plan #539-007D-0060 featured on page 16.

HDA
INC

COVER HOME - The home shown on the front cover is Plan #539-022D-0014, featured on page 10, and courtesy of Lifestyle Home Design. The apartment garage is Plan #539-009D-7516 and is featured on page 265.

LOWE'S SMALLER LOT HOME PLANS
is published by HDA, Inc., 944 Anglum Road, St. Louis, MO, 63042. All rights reserved. Reproduction in whole or in part without written permission of the publisher is prohibited. Printed in U.S.A. © 2010. Artist drawings and photos shown in this publication may vary slightly from the actual working drawings. Some photos are shown in mirror reverse. Please refer to the floor plan for accurate layout.

ISBN-13: 978-1-58678-142-2

Current Printing

10 9 8 7 6 5 4 3 2 1

HDA, Inc.
944 Anglum Rd.
St. Louis, Missouri 63042
corporate website - www.hdainc.com

Contents

Plan #539-022D-0014 featured on page 10.

We understand that it is difficult to find blueprints that will meet all your needs. That is why HDA, Inc. is pleased to offer plan modification services.

Thinking About Customizing Your Plan?

If you're like many customers, you may want to make changes to your home plan to make it the dream home you've always wanted. That's where our expert design and modification team comes in. You won't find a more efficient and economic way to get your changes done than by using our design services.

Whether it's enlarging a kitchen, adding a porch or converting a crawl space to a basement, we can customize any plan and make it perfect for your family. Simply create your wish list and let us go to work. Soon you'll have the blueprints for your new home and at a fraction of the cost of hiring an architect!

The HDA Modification Advantage

- We can customize any of the thousands of plans on www.houseplansandmore.com.
- FREE cost estimates for your home plan modifications within 24 hours (Monday-Friday, 8am-5pm CST).
- Average turn-around time to complete the modifications is 2-3 weeks.
- One-on-one design consultations.

Customizing Facts

- The average cost for us to customize a house plan is typically less than 1 percent of the building costs — compare that to the national average of 7 percent of building costs.
- The average modification cost for a home is typically $800 to $1,500 (this does not include the cost of the reproducible blueprint, which is required to make plan changes).
- The average cost to modify a project plan is typically between $200-$500.

Other Helpful Information

- Feel free to include a sketch, or a specific list of changes you'd like to make.
- One of our designers will contact you within 24 hours with your free estimate.
- Upon accepting the estimate, you will need to purchase the reproducible set of plans.
- A contract, which includes a specific list of changes and fees will be sent to you for approval.
- Upon approving the contract, our designers will keep you up to date by emailing or faxing sketches throughout the project.
- Plan can be converted to metric.
- Barrier Free Conversion (accommodating a plan for special needs, transforming your living space for everyone).
- Customizing is also available for project plans, such as sheds, garages, apartment garages and more.

3 Easy Steps For Fast Service

1. Visit **www.houseplansandmore.com** to download the modification request form, complete the form and email it to customize@hdainc.com.
2. Fax the completed modification form to 651-602-5050.
3. Call 888-355-5728 for your free estimate.

If you are not able to access the internet, please call 1-877-379-3420 (Monday-Friday, 8am-5pm CST).

Choosing a home plan is an exciting but difficult task. Many factors play a role in what home plan is best for you and your family. To help you get started, we have pinpointed some of the major factors to consider when searching for your dream home. Take the time to evaluate your family's needs and you will have an easier time sorting through all of the home plans offered in this book.

Budget: The first thing to consider is your budget. Many items take part in this budget, from ordering the blueprints to the last doorknob purchased. When you find your dream home plan, visit your commercial sales specialist at your local Lowe's store to get a cost-to-build estimate to ensure that the finished product will be within your cost range.

Family Lifestyle: After your budget is deciphered, you need to assess you and your family's lifestyle needs. Think about the stage of life you are at now, and what stages you will be going through in the future. Ask yourself questions to figure out how much room you need now and if you will need room for expansion. Are you married? Do you have children? How many children do you plan on having? Are you an empty-nester?

Incorporate in your planning any frequent guests you may have, including elderly parents, grandchildren or adult children who may live with you.

Does your family entertain a lot? If so, think about the rooms you will need to do so. Will you need both formal and informal spaces? Do you need a gourmet kitchen? Do you need a game room and/or a wet bar?

> **Experts in the field suggest that the best way to determine your needs is to begin by listing everything you like or dislike about your current home.**

Floor Plan Layouts: When looking through our home plans, imagine yourself walking through the house. Consider the flow from the entry to the living, sleeping and gathering areas. Does the layout ensure privacy for the master bedroom? Does the garage enter near the kitchen for easy unloading? Does the placement of the windows provide enough privacy from any neighboring properties? Do you plan on using furniture you already have? Will this furniture fit in the appropriate rooms? When you find a plan you want to purchase, be sure to picture yourself actually living in it.

Exterior Spaces: There are many different home styles ranging from Traditional to Contemporary. Flip through and find which style most appeals to you and the neighborhood in which you plan to build. Also think of your site and how the entire house will fit on this site. Picture any landscaping you plan on incorporating into the design. Using your imagination is key when choosing a home plan.

Choosing a home plan can be an intimidating experience. Asking yourself these questions before you get started on the search will help you through the process. With our large selection of multiple styles we are certain you will find your dream home in the following pages.

The Lowe's Legacy Series

Leg·a·cy: Something that is handed down or remains for generations

HDA, Inc. is proud to introduce to you the Lowe's Legacy Series. The home plans in this collection carry on the Lowe's tradition of quality and expertise, and will continue to do so for many generations.

Choosing a home plan can be a daunting task. With the Legacy Series, we will set your mind at ease. Selecting a plan from this group will ensure a home designed with the Lowe's standard of excellence, creating a dream home for you and your family.

This collection of Legacy Series plans includes our most popular smaller lot home plans. Browse through the pages to discover a home with the options and special characteristics you need.

Along with one-of-a-kind craftsmanship, all Legacy Series home plans offer industry-leading material lists. These accurate material lists will save you a considerable amount of time and money, providing you with the quantity, dimensions and descriptions of the major building materials necessary to construct your home. You'll get faster and more accurate bids from your contractor while saving money by paying for only the materials you need.

The Lowe's Legacy Series is the perfect place to start your search for the home of your dreams. You will find the expected beauty you want and the functional efficiency you need, all designed with unmatched quality.

Turn the page and begin the wonderful journey of finding your new home.

Photos clockwise from top: 539-022D-0014, page 10; 539-027D-0005, page 17; 539-072L-0003, page 19; 539-007D-0060, page 16.

Building on a Smaller Lot

Contradictory to the rampant idea of "bigger is better;" more people are investing in small lots to build their dream homes.

*F*or some it is most affordable, others desire proximity to specific locales, and some see small lots as a way to reduce their ecological footprint. Whatever the reason, the same is true for all – smaller lots are not about less space. It is intelligent building with some extra creativity thrown in for good measure. The challenges presented by building on small lots are nothing to be discouraged by, and the sacrifices are less than one may anticipate. Think new options rather than fewer options!

Smaller lot homes are considered to be 50 feet (or less) wide. Small lot homes can be positioned in a variety of ways to maximize the land use. The most efficient use of space for a small lot home is building two stories. This is more economical as there will be greater space without additional foundation or roofing expenses.

Small lot homes often have small yards that homeowners choose to landscape creatively, accent with cozy porches, or convert to larger patios that allow for perfect entertaining possibilities. If small home lots are grouped together, a community courtyard may be in place rather than individual yards, with garages accessed from the rear via an alleyway. Along with yards, garages are typically the greatest challenge to small lot designers. In addition to highly functional rear garages, front garages with accented doors eliminate excessive driveway space without diminishing the home's beauty.

Inside small lot homes, efficiency is at a premium. Every nook and cranny is used to its fullest potential, eliminating storage concerns and dread of lost personal space. Even windows are placed strategically, some allowing five times more light inside, expanding the home's spatial feel. Design is just as significant, if not more so, in comparison to size.

Small lot homes are not inferior, limiting, or restricted to uniformity. They are quite capable of being fully accessorized inside and out, in addition to being particularly affordable.

Dream homes, like dreams themselves, come in all sizes.

Plan #539-007D-0054, see page 13.

Plan #539-022D-0007, see page 31.

Plan #539-072L-0015, see page 26.

LOWE'S
LEGACY
SERIES

Timeless Country Style

- 1,553 total square feet of living area

- Two-story living area creates an open and airy feel to the interior especially with two dormers above

- First floor master bedroom is private and includes its own bath and walk-in closet

- Two secondary bedrooms share a full bath with double vanity

- 3 bedrooms, 2 1/2 baths, 2-car drive under garage

- Walk-out basement foundation

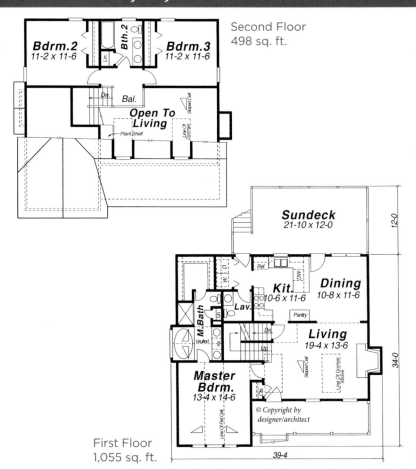

Second Floor
498 sq. ft.

Bdrm.2
11-2 x 11-6

Bth.2

Bdrm.3
11-2 x 11-6

Dn. | Bal.

Open To Living

Plant Shelf

Sundeck
21-10 x 12-0

Kit.
10-6 x 11-6

Dining
10-8 x 11-6

Lav.

Pantry

M.Bath

Living
19-4 x 13-6

Master Bdrm.
13-4 x 14-6

© Copyright by designer/architect

First Floor
1,055 sq. ft.

39-4

Country Kitchen Is Center Of Living Activities

- 1,556 total square feet of living area

- A compact home with all the amenities

- Country kitchen combines practicality with access to other areas for eating and entertaining

- Two-way fireplace joins the dining and living areas

- A plant shelf and vaulted ceiling highlight the master bedroom

- 3 bedrooms, 2 1/2 baths, 2-car garage

- Basement foundation

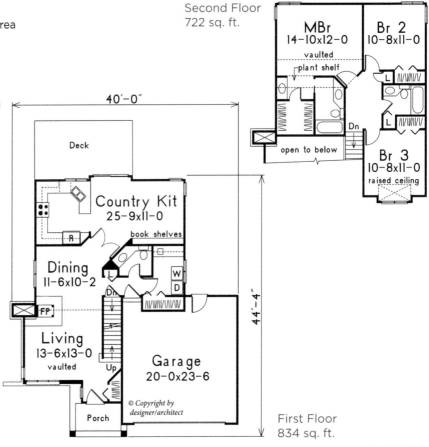

Second Floor
722 sq. ft.

MBr
14-10x12-0
vaulted
plant shelf

Br 2
10-8x11-0

open to below

Dn

Br 3
10-8x11-0
raised ceiling

40'-0"

Deck

Country Kit
25-9x11-0

book shelves

Dining
11-6x10-2

W
D

FP

Dn

Living
13-6x13-0
vaulted

Up

Garage
20-0x23-6

44'-4"

© Copyright by
designer/architect

Porch

First Floor
834 sq. ft.

Great Room Window Adds Character Inside And Out

- 1,368 total square feet of living area
- Entry foyer steps down to an open living area that combines the great room and formal dining area
- Vaulted master bedroom includes a box-bay window and a bath with a large vanity, separate tub and shower
- Cozy breakfast area features direct access to the patio and pass-through kitchen
- Handy linen closet is located in the hall
- 3 bedrooms, 2 baths, 2-car garage
- Basement foundation

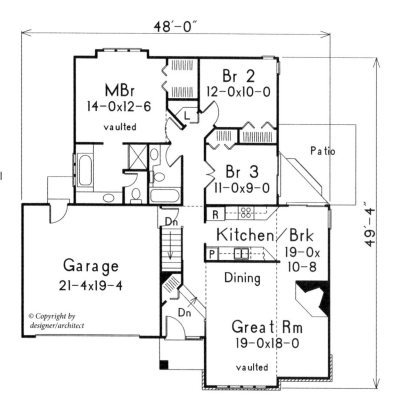

Exterior Accents Complement Front Facade

- 2,282 total square feet of living area
- Balcony and two-story foyer add spaciousness to this compact plan
- First floor master bedroom has a corner tub in the large private bath
- Out-of-the-way kitchen is open to the full-windowed breakfast room
- 4 bedrooms, 2 1/2 baths, 2-car drive under side entry garage
- Basement foundation

Second Floor
851 sq. ft.

open to below

Balcony

Br 4
11-6x16-10

Dn

L

Br 3
11-6x11-2

Br 2
10-8x13-6

open to below

Deck

© Copyright by designer/architect

Brk
11-6x8-6

sloped clg

Kit
11-6x 9-0

R

Family
19-8x13-6

D

W

32'-0"

Dining
11-6x11-6

P

Dn

Up Foyer

Living
11-6x13-6

MBr
15-8x13-6

First Floor
1,431 sq. ft.

50'-0"

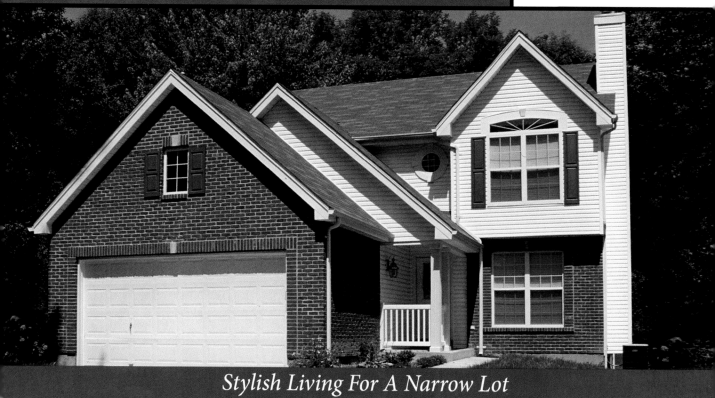

Stylish Living For A Narrow Lot

- 1,575 total square feet of living area
- Inviting porch leads to spacious living and dining rooms
- Kitchen with corner windows features an island snack bar, attractive breakfast room bay, convenient laundry area and built-in pantry
- A luxury bath and walk-in closet adorn the master bedroom suite
- 3 bedrooms, 2 1/2 baths, 2-car garage
- Basement foundation, drawings also include crawl space and slab foundations

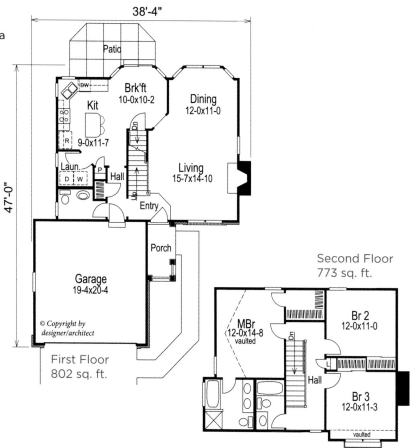

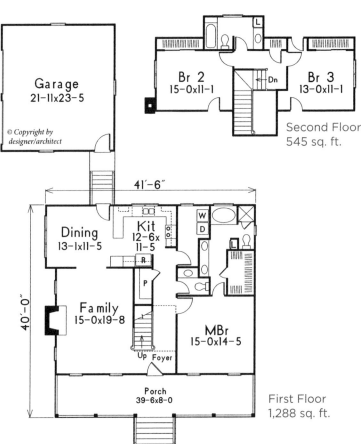

Two-Story Foyer Adds Spacious Feeling

- 1,833 total square feet of living area

- Large master bedroom includes a spacious bath with garden tub, separate shower and large walk-in closet

- The spacious dining area is brightened by large windows and outdoor access

- Detached two-car garage with walkway leading to house adds charm to this country home

- 3 bedrooms, 2 1/2 baths, 2-car detached side entry garage

- Crawl space foundation, drawings also include slab foundation

Garage
21-11x23-5

© Copyright by
designer/architect

Br 2
15-0x11-1

Dn

Br 3
13-0x11-1

Second Floor
545 sq. ft.

41'-6"

40'-0"

Dining
13-1x11-5

Kit
12-6x
11-5

W D

Family
15-0x19-8

MBr
15-0x14-5

Up Foyer

Porch
39-6x8-0

First Floor
1,288 sq. ft.

Desirable, Traditional Brick Home

- 1,897 total square feet of living area
- A high ceiling tops the terrific great room with a fireplace centered on one wall
- A large breakfast room is just steps away from the kitchen for convenience
- All the bedrooms are located on the second floor for convenience with family living
- 3 bedrooms, 2 1/2 baths, 2-car garage
- Basement foundation

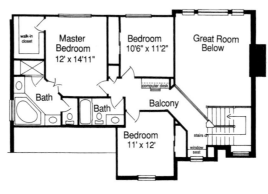

Second Floor
861 sq. ft.

First Floor
1,036 sq. ft.

Plan #539-007D-0060 • **Price Code B**

Distinguished Styling For A Small Lot

- 1,268 total square feet of living area

- Multiple gables, large porch and arched windows create a classy exterior

- Innovative design provides openness in the great room, kitchen and breakfast room

- Secondary bedrooms have private hall with bath

- 2" x 6" exterior walls available, please order plan #539-007E-0060

- Plan also available with energy efficient R-Control® SIPs (Structural Insulated Panels), please call 1-877-379-3420 for more information

- 3 bedrooms, 2 baths, 2-car garage

- Basement foundation, drawings also include crawl space and slab foundations

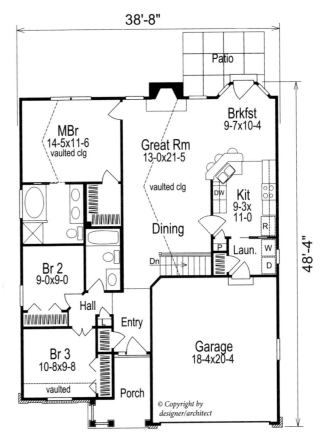

38'-8"

48'-4"

Patio

MBr
14-5x11-6
vaulted clg

Brkfst
9-7x10-4

Great Rm
13-0x21-5
vaulted clg

Kit
9-3x
11-0

Dining

Br 2
9-0x9-0

Laun.

Dn

Hall

Entry

Br 3
10-8x9-8

Garage
18-4x20-4

vaulted

Porch

© Copyright by
designer/architect

Open Rooms Throughout Home

- 2,135 total square feet of living area
- The family room features extra space, an impressive fireplace and full wall of windows that joins the breakfast room creating a spacious entertainment area
- Washer and dryer are conveniently located on the second floor near the bedrooms
- The kitchen features an island counter and pantry
- 4 bedrooms, 2 1/2 baths, 2-car garage
- Basement foundation

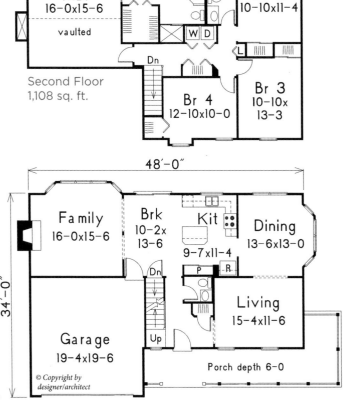

Second Floor
1,108 sq. ft.

First Floor
1,027 sq. ft.

Exceptional Narrow-Lot Home

- 2,113 total square feet of living area
- Formal living and dining rooms combine to the left of the foyer for an elegant entertaining atmosphere
- At the rear of the house, the family room, breakfast area and kitchen flow together for a casual gathering space
- All the bedrooms are located on the second floor for extra peace and quiet
- 4 bedrooms, 2 1/2 baths, 2-car garage
- Basement foundation, drawings also include walk-out basement foundation

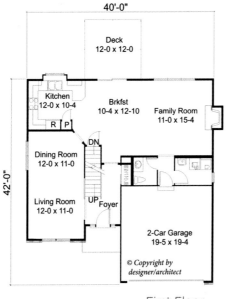

First Floor
1,080 sq. ft.

Second Floor
1,033 sq. ft.

Great Curb Appeal Gives A Solid Look

- 1,317 total square feet of living area
- A large window topped by a clerestory window gives the living room a bright, airy feel
- A three-way fireplace defines the space between the living and dining rooms
- An efficient kitchen neatly serves the dining room
- 3 bedrooms, 2 baths, 2-car garage
- Basement foundation

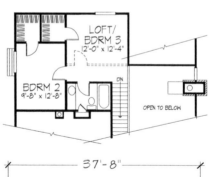

Second Floor
423 sq. ft.

First Floor
894 sq. ft.

Rear Stairway Smooths Traffic Flow

- 2,195 total square feet of living area
- Striking facade provided by gracious two-story window treatment
- Bay windows add light and space
- Open family and kitchen/breakfast area exits onto the spacious rear deck
- 4 bedrooms, 2 1/2 baths, 2-car drive under side entry garage
- Basement foundation

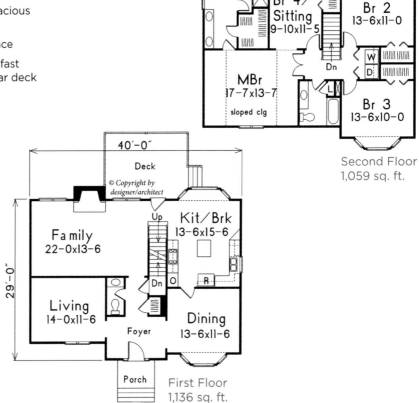

Br 4/
Sitting
9-10x11-5

Br 2
13-6x11-0

MBr
17-7x13-7
sloped clg

Dn

W
D

Br 3
13-6x10-0

Second Floor
1,059 sq. ft.

40'-0"

Deck

© Copyright by
designer/architect

Family
22-0x13-6

Up

Kit/Brk
13-6x15-6

29'-0"

Dn

R

Living
14-0x11-6

Dn

Dining
13-6x11-6

Foyer

Porch

First Floor
1,136 sq. ft.

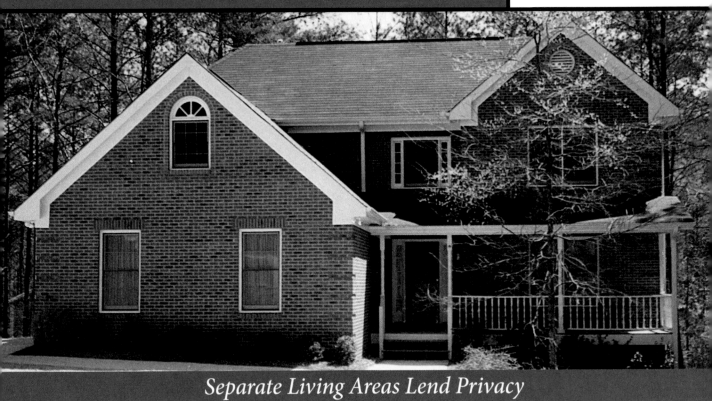

Separate Living Areas Lend Privacy

- 2,300 total square feet of living area
- Large, open foyer creates a grand entrance
- Convenient open breakfast area includes peninsula counter, bay window and easy access to the deck
- Dining and living rooms flow together for expanded entertaining space
- Bonus room on the second floor has an additional 254 square feet of living area
- 3 bedrooms, 2 1/2 baths, 2-car side entry garage
- Walk-out basement foundation, drawings also include slab and crawl space foundations

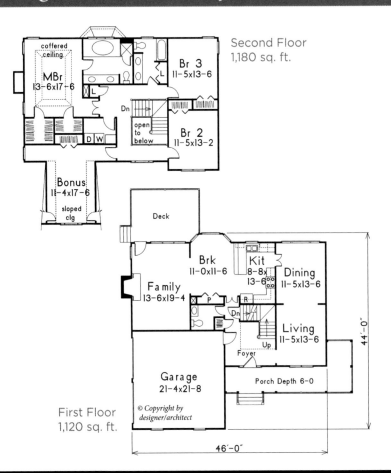

Second Floor
1,180 sq. ft.

First Floor
1,120 sq. ft.

© Copyright by designer/architect

Rambling Country Bungalow

- 1,475 total square feet of living area
- Family room features a high ceiling and prominent corner fireplace
- Kitchen with island counter and garden window makes a convenient connection between the family and dining rooms
- Hallway leads to three bedrooms all with large walk-in closets
- Covered breezeway joins the main house and garage
- Full-width covered porch entry lends a country touch
- 3 bedrooms, 2 baths, 2-car detached side entry garage
- Slab foundation, drawings also include crawl space foundation

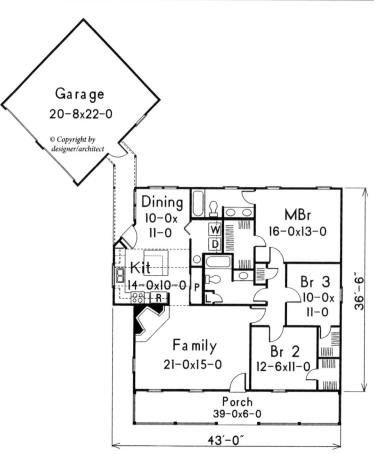

Garage
20-8x22-0

© Copyright by designer/architect

Dining
10-0x 11-0

MBr
16-0x13-0

W D

Kit
14-0x10-0

Br 3
10-0x 11-0

Family
21-0x15-0

Br 2
12-6x11-0

Porch
39-0x6-0

36'-6"

43'-0"

Brick And Siding Combine For A Decorative Exterior

- 1,739 total square feet of living area
- The secluded kitchen is a chef's dream and stays bright with corner windows
- The oversized living room includes space for an optional fireplace and enjoys sliding glass doors leading to the rear deck
- The master bedroom features a private vanity and tub while sharing the first floor half bath
- 3 bedrooms, 2 baths, 2-car garage
- Basement foundation

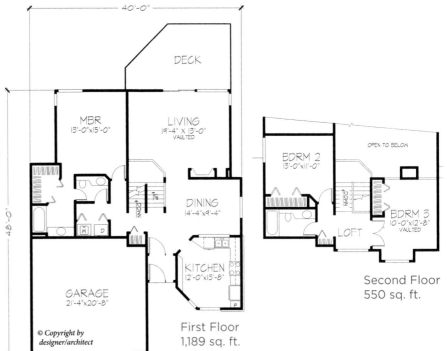

First Floor
1,189 sq. ft.

Second Floor
550 sq. ft.

Spacious Vaulted Great Room

- 1,189 total square feet of living area
- All bedrooms are located on the second floor
- Dining room and kitchen both have views of the patio
- Convenient half bath is located near the kitchen
- Master bedroom has a private bath
- 3 bedrooms, 2 1/2 baths, 2-car garage
- Basement foundation

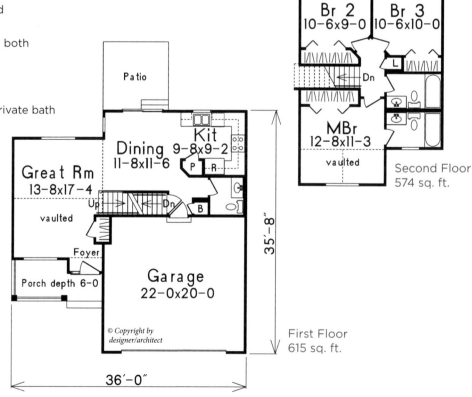

Patio

Kit
9-8x9-2

Dining
11-8x11-6

Great Rm
13-8x17-4

vaulted

Up   Dn   B

Foyer

Porch depth 6-0

Garage
22-0x20-0

© Copyright by designer/architect

35'-8"

36'-0"

Br 2
10-6x9-0

Br 3
10-6x10-0

L   Dn

MBr
12-8x11-3

vaulted

Second Floor
574 sq. ft.

First Floor
615 sq. ft.

Stunning Two-Story

- 1,602 total square feet of living area
- The vaulted living room shines with a two-story window and grand fireplace
- Columns define the entry into the formal dining room
- A double-door entry adds elegance to the master suite that also enjoys two closets and a private bath
- 3 bedrooms, 2 1/2 baths, 2-car garage
- Basement foundation

First Floor
1,112 sq. ft.

Second Floor
490 sq. ft.

Vaulted Master Bedroom

- 1,252 total square feet of living area
- This delightful ranch features stylish amenities provided for easy family living
- The living room shares a vaulted ceiling and high plant shelf with the dining room, along with a fireplace and sliding glass doors to the deck
- The centrally located kitchen is open to the dining room for easy serving
- 3 bedrooms, 2 baths, 2-car garage
- Basement foundation

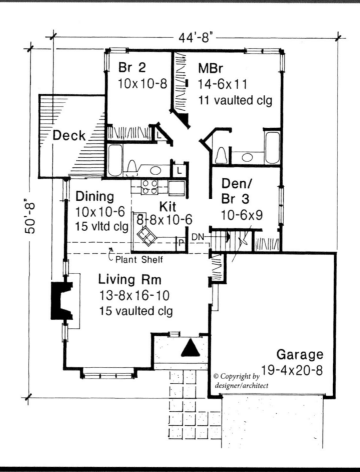

High-Style Compact Plan

- 2,356 total square feet of living area
- Impressive arched and mullioned window treatment embellishes the entrance and foyer
- Bedroom #4 is located above the side entry garage and has access to the attic
- Full-size laundry facility
- Adjoining family room, breakfast area and kitchen form an extensive living area
- 4 bedrooms, 2 1/2 baths, 2-car side entry garage
- Basement foundation

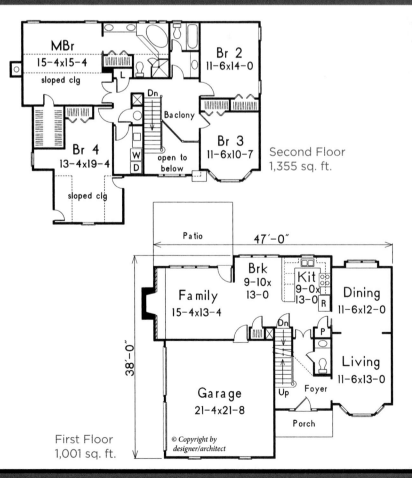

MBr
15-4x15-4
sloped clg

Br 2
11-6x14-0

Dn

Balcony

Br 4
13-4x19-4

W
D

open to below

Br 3
11-6x10-7

Second Floor
1,355 sq. ft.

sloped clg

Patio

47'-0"

Brk
9-10x
13-0

Kit
9-0x
13-0

Dining
11-6x12-0

Family
15-4x13-4

Dn

P

38'-0"

Living
11-6x13-0

Up

Foyer

Garage
21-4x21-8

Porch

© Copyright by
designer/architect

First Floor
1,001 sq. ft.

Rear Patio Creates Outdoor Living Space

- 1,524 total square feet of living area
- Delightful balcony overlooks the two-story entry illuminated by an oval window
- Roomy first floor master bedroom offers quiet privacy
- All bedrooms feature one or more walk-in closets
- 3 bedrooms, 2 1/2 baths, 2-car garage
- Basement foundation, drawings also include crawl space and slab foundations

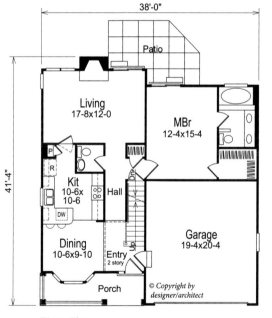

First Floor
951 sq. ft.

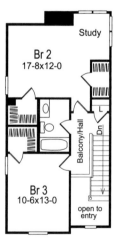

Second Floor
573 sq. ft.

Lovely Circle-Top Windows

- 1,368 total square feet of living area
- The bedrooms are tucked at the rear of the home for peace and quiet
- The great room has a cozy corner fireplace and a lovely bayed window treatment
- A glorious patio can be reached from the kitchen/breakfast room
- 3 bedrooms, 2 baths, 2-car garage
- Basement foundation

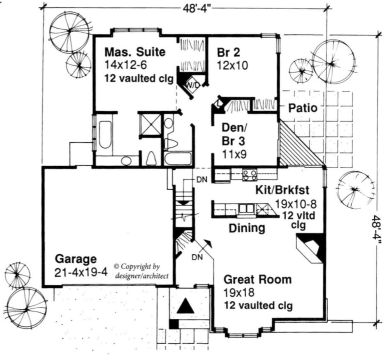

Ideal Home For Lake, Mountain Or Seaside

- 1,711 total square feet of living area
- Entry leads to a vaulted great room with exposed beams, two-story window wall, see-through fireplace, wet bar and outdoor deck
- Bayed breakfast area shares the fireplace and joins a sun-drenched kitchen and deck
- Vaulted first floor master bedroom features a double-door entry, two closets and bookshelves
- Spiral stairs and a balcony dramatize the loft that doubles as a spacious second bedroom
- 2 bedrooms, 2 1/2 baths
- Basement foundation

Second Floor
397 sq. ft.

First Floor
1,314 sq. ft.

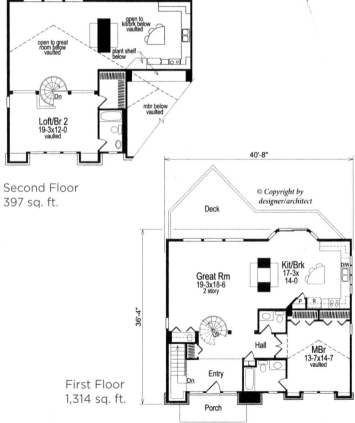

© Copyright by designer/architect

Contemporary Design For Open Family Living

- 1,516 total square feet of living area
- All living and dining areas are interconnected for a spacious look and easy movement
- Covered entrance leads into the sunken great room with a rugged corner fireplace
- Family kitchen combines practicality with access to other areas
- Second floor loft opens to rooms below and can convert to a third bedroom
- The dormer in bedroom #2 adds interest
- 2 bedrooms, 2 1/2 baths, 2-car garage
- Basement foundation

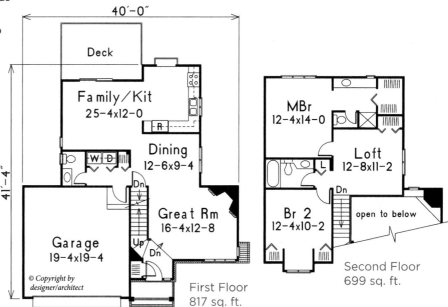

40'-0"

41'-4"

Deck

Family/Kit
25-4x12-0

Dining
12-6x9-4

Great Rm
16-4x12-8

Garage
19-4x19-4

© Copyright by designer/architect

W D

Dn

Up

Dn

First Floor
817 sq. ft.

MBr
12-4x14-0

Loft
12-8x11-2

Br 2
12-4x10-2

Dn

open to below

Second Floor
699 sq. ft.

Lake House With Space For A Boat, Two Jet-Skis And A Car

- 1,498 total square feet of living area
- A perfect home for a narrow and sloping lot featuring both front and rear garages
- Large living room has fireplace, rear outdoor balcony and a pass-through snack bar to a spacious U-shaped kitchen with adjacent dining area
- Roomy master bedroom with luxury bath and two walk-in closets
- 2 bedrooms, 2 1/2 baths, 1-car garage and a 2-car rear entry drive under garage
- Walk-out basement foundation

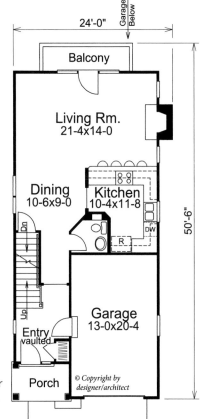

24'-0"

Garage Below

Balcony

Living Rm.
21-4x14-0

Dining
10-6x9-0

Kitchen
10-4x11-8

DW

R

50'-6"

Dn

Up

Garage
13-0x20-4

Entry
vaulted

First Floor
827 sq. ft.

Porch

© Copyright by
designer/architect

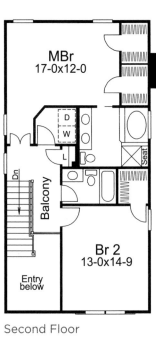

MBr
17-0x12-0

D
W

L

Seat

Dn

Balcony

Br 2
13-0x14-9

Entry
below

Second Floor
671 sq. ft.

Spacious Great Room

- 1,308 total square feet of living area

- A lovely bay window and access to the rear patio are some of the features of the vaulted kitchen/dining area

- A tall ceiling and warming fireplace in the great room appeals to every homeowner

- The vaulted master bedroom showcases a large walk-in closet, bay window and private bath

- 3 bedrooms, 2 baths, 2-car detached garage

- Basement foundation

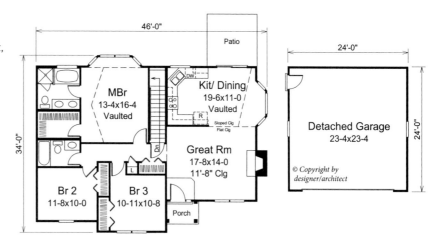

Layout Features All The Essentials For Comfortable Living

- 1,344 total square feet of living area
- Kitchen has side entry, laundry area, pantry and joins the family/dining/kitchen area
- Master bedroom includes a private bath
- Linen and storage closets in hall
- Covered porch opens to the spacious living room with a handy coat closet
- 3 bedrooms, 2 baths
- Crawl space foundation, drawings also include basement and slab foundations

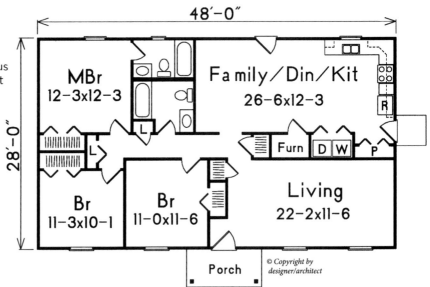

48'-0"

28'-0"

MBr
12-3x12-3

Family/Din/Kit
26-6x12-3

Furn D W P

Br
11-3x10-1

Br
11-0x11-6

Living
22-2x11-6

Porch

© Copyright by designer/architect

Compact And Simple

- 1,647 total square feet of living area
- Enormous great room boasts a vaulted ceiling
- Located in the great room is an open kitchen with an island and breakfast bar
- Stunning loft overlooks the great room
- 2 bedrooms, 1 bath
- Slab foundation

BEDROOM 1
11'-10" x 10'-0"

BEDROOM 2
11'-4" x 10'-0"

COATS

W/D

LINEN

PANTRY

46'-0"
+ PORCH

GREAT ROOM
27'-4" x 29'-5"
20' HIGH CEILING

VAULT

VAULT

DECK/PATIO
11'-6" x 18'-8"

DECK
7'-6" x 36'-0"

PORCH
24'-4" x 7'-6"

© Copyright by
designer/architect

28'-0"
+ DECKS/PATIO

First Floor
1,288 sq. ft.

VAULT

VAULT

LOFT
23'-1" x 15'-6"

40" KNEE WALL

DN

OPEN BELOW
20' HIGH CEILING

VAULT

VAULT

Second Floor
359 sq. ft.

Plenty Of Family Gathering Areas

- 1,941 total square feet of living area

- Dramatic, exciting and spacious interior

- Vaulted great room is brightened by a sunken atrium window wall and skylights

- Vaulted U-shaped gourmet kitchen with plant shelf opens to the dining room

- First floor half bath features space for a stackable washer and dryer

- 4 bedrooms, 2 1/2 baths, 2-car garage

- Walk-out basement foundation

First Floor
996 sq. ft.

Lower Level
945 sq. ft.

© Copyright by designer/architect

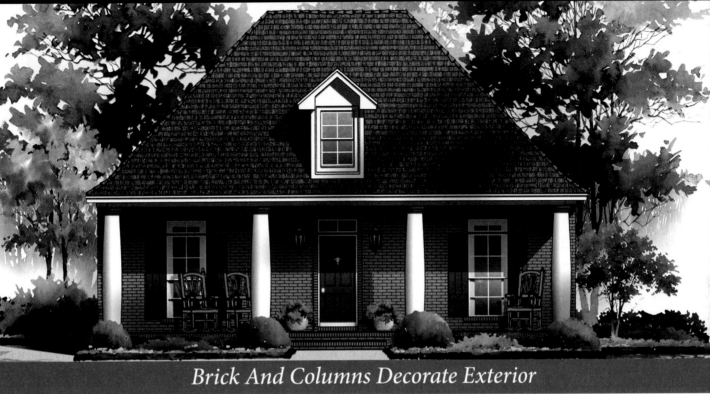

Brick And Columns Decorate Exterior

- 1,650 total square feet of living area

- The private master bedroom enjoys a whirlpool tub, walk-in closet and twin vanities

- The expansive great room is topped with a tray ceiling and also includes a built-in entertainment center and easy access to the kitchen and dining room

- A laundry room, walk-in hall closet and flex space offer the convenience every family needs

- 3 bedrooms, 2 baths, 2-car side entry garage

- Crawl space foundation, drawings also include slab foundation

Width: 35'-0"
Depth: 73'-4"

Two Car Garage
20-4 x 21-8

Storage

8' Ceiling
Jet Tub

Master Bath
13-8 x 8-10
10-0 Ceiling

Van.

Lin.

Shr.

© Copyright by designer/architect

Kitchen
12-6 x 14-6

Island

W D
Util.
6-8 x 6-4

Pan./Cab's

Master Bedroom
14-6 x 13-4
10-0 Ceiling

Clos.
6-8 x 7-10

Clos.

Bedroom #2
11-6 x 11-0
10-0 Ceiling

Dining Room
12-6 x 12-4
10-0 Ceiling

Flex Space
6-8 x 7-8

Hall

Hall Bath

Tub/Shr.

Entertainment Center

Trayed Ceiling

Great Room
19-0 x 15-6
11-0 Ceiling

Clos.

Bedroom #3
11-6 x 11-0
10-0 Ceiling

Covered Porch
35-0 x 8-0

Well-Sculptured Design, Inside And Out

- 1,759 total square feet of living area
- The striking entry is created by a unique stair layout, an open high ceiling and a fireplace
- Second floor bedrooms share a private dressing area and bath
- Bonus area over garage, which is included in the square footage, could easily convert to a fourth bedroom or activity center
- 3 bedrooms, 2 1/2 baths, 2-car garage
- Basement foundation

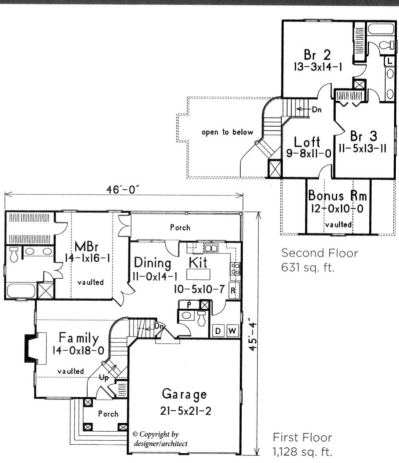

Second Floor
631 sq. ft.

First Floor
1,128 sq. ft.

© Copyright by
designer/architect

Plan #539-058D-0038 • **Price Code B**

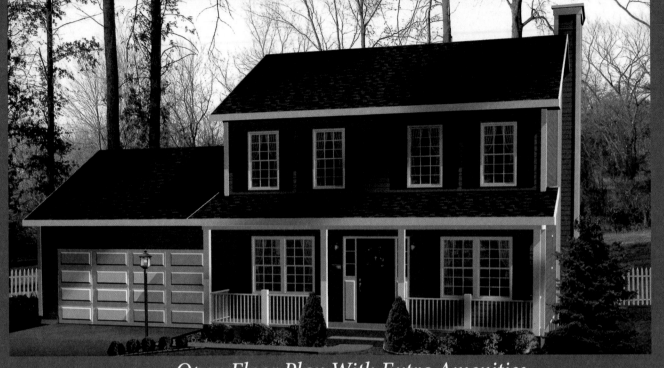

Open Floor Plan With Extra Amenities

- 1,680 total square feet of living area
- Compact and efficient layout in an affordable package
- Second floor has three bedrooms all with oversized closets
- All bedrooms are located on the second floor for privacy
- 3 bedrooms, 2 1/2 baths, 2-car garage
- Basement foundation

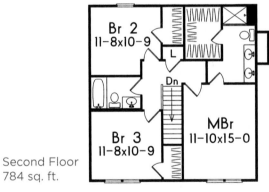

Second Floor
784 sq. ft.

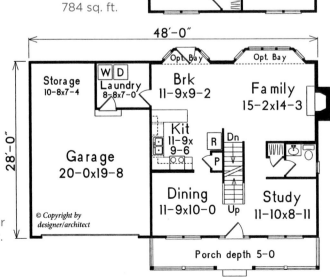

First Floor
896 sq. ft.

Country Home With Gracious Proportions

- 2,054 total square feet of living area
- A sweeping porch leads to the large foyer with staircase, powder room and handy coat closet
- Spacious living room has a fireplace, patio access and an adjacent computer room
- Kitchen features a snack bar, island counter, pantry and breakfast area with bay window
- Large master bedroom has two spacious closets and accesses a luxury bath with separate toilet and corner tub
- 3 bedrooms, 2 1/2 baths, 2-car detached garage
- Basement foundation

Second Floor
1,020 sq. ft.

First Floor
1,034 sq. ft.

Small Home Is Remarkably Spacious

- 914 total square feet of living area
- Large porch for leisure evenings
- Dining area with bay window, open stairs and a pass-through kitchen create openness
- Basement includes generous garage space, a storage area, finished laundry and mechanical room
- 2 bedrooms, 1 bath, 2-car drive under rear entry garage
- Basement foundation

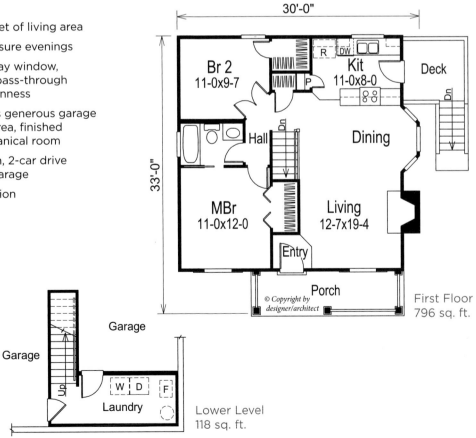

© Copyright by designer/architect

First Floor
796 sq. ft.

Lower Level
118 sq. ft.

Impressive Two-Story Entry Boasts Popular T-Stairs

- 2,336 total square feet of living area
- Stately sunken living room with partially vaulted ceiling and classic arched transom windows create a pleasant atmosphere
- Family room features plenty of windows and a fireplace with flanking bookshelves
- All bedrooms are located on the second floor for added privacy
- 4 bedrooms, 2 1/2 baths, 2-car garage
- Basement foundation, drawings also include slab and crawl space foundations

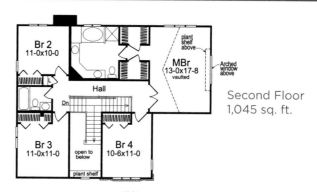

Second Floor
1,045 sq. ft.

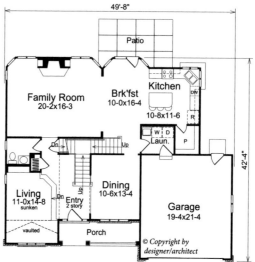

First Floor
1,291 sq. ft.

LOWE'S
LEGACY
SERIES

Quaint Country Home Is Ideal

- 1,028 total square feet of living area
- Well-designed bath contains laundry facilities
- L-shaped kitchen has a handy pantry
- Tall windows flank the family room fireplace
- Cozy covered porch provides a unique angled entry into this home
- 3 bedrooms, 1 bath
- Crawl space foundation

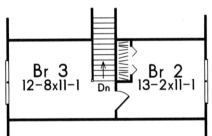

Br 3
12-8x11-1

Dn

Br 2
13-2x11-1

Second Floor
300 sq. ft.

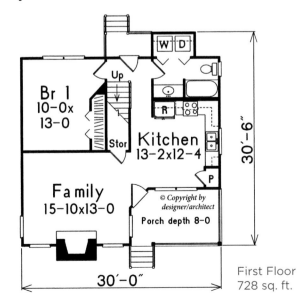

W | D

Up

Br 1
10-0x
13-0

Stor

R

Kitchen
13-2x12-4

30'-6"

Family
15-10x13-0

© Copyright by
designer/architect

Porch depth 8-0

P

30'-0"

First Floor
728 sq. ft.

Dramatic Sloping Ceiling In Living Room

- 1,432 total square feet of living area
- Energy efficient home with 2" x 6" exterior walls
- Enter the two-story foyer from the covered porch or garage
- Living room has a square bay window with seat, glazed end wall with floor-to-ceiling windows and access to the deck
- Kitchen/dining room also opens to the deck for added convenience
- 3 bedrooms, 2 baths, 1-car garage
- Basement foundation, drawings also include slab foundation

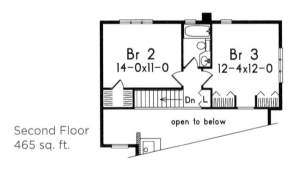

Second Floor
465 sq. ft.

Br 2
14-0x11-0

Br 3
12-4x12-0

open to below

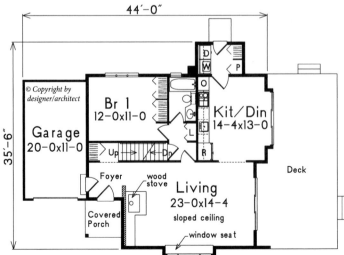

44'-0"

35'-6"

© Copyright by designer/architect

Garage
20-0x11-0

Br 1
12-0x11-0

Kit/Din
14-4x13-0

Deck

Foyer

wood stove

Living
23-0x14-4
sloped ceiling

Covered Porch

window seat

First Floor
967 sq. ft.

Perfect Vacation Home

- 1,230 total square feet of living area
- Spacious living room accesses the huge deck
- Bedroom #3 features a balcony overlooking the deck
- Kitchen with dining area accesses the outdoors
- Washer and dryer are tucked under the stairs for space efficiency
- 3 bedrooms, 1 bath
- Crawl space foundation, drawings also include slab foundation

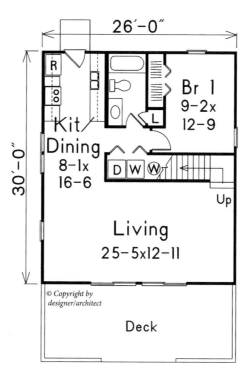

First Floor
780 sq. ft.

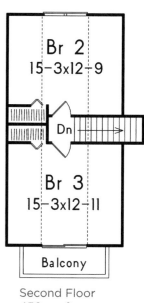

Second Floor
450 sq. ft.

Breakfast Bay Area Opens To Deck

- 1,020 total square feet of living area
- Kitchen features open stairs, pass-through to great room, pantry and deck access
- Master bedroom features private entrance to bath, large walk-in closet and sliding doors to deck
- Informal entrance into home through the garage
- Great room has a vaulted ceiling and fireplace
- 2 bedrooms, 1 bath, 2-car garage
- Basement foundation

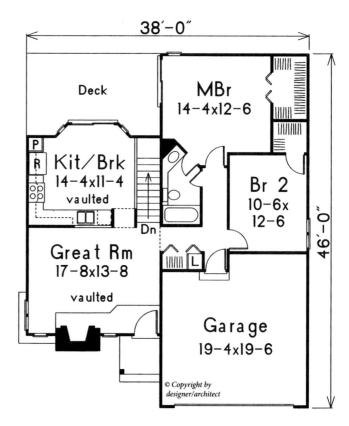

38'-0"

46'-0"

Deck

MBr
14-4x12-6

Kit/Brk
14-4x11-4
vaulted

Br 2
10-6x
12-6

Dn

Great Rm
17-8x13-8

vaulted

Garage
19-4x19-6

© Copyright by
designer/architect

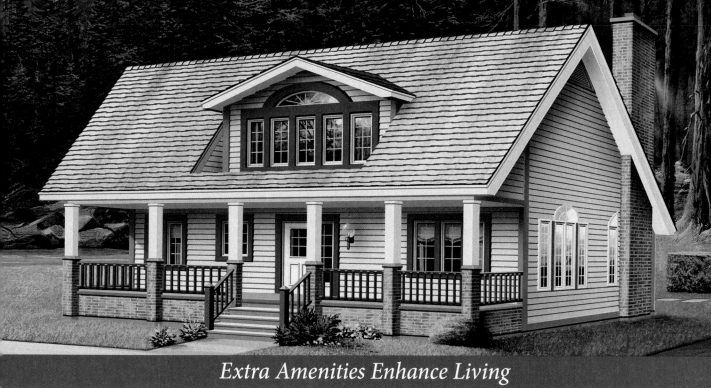

Extra Amenities Enhance Living

- 2,009 total square feet of living area
- Spacious master bedroom has a dramatic sloped ceiling and private bath with a double-bowl vanity and walk-in closet
- Bedroom #3 has an extra storage area behind the closet
- Versatile screened porch is ideal for entertaining all year-round
- Sunny breakfast area is located near the kitchen and screened porch for convenience
- 3 bedrooms, 2 1/2 baths
- Basement foundation

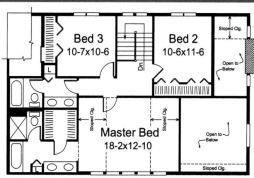

Second Floor
847 sq. ft.

First Floor
1,162 sq. ft.

Perfect Vacation Cabin

- 1,020 total square feet of living area
- The extra-wide porch offers an enchanting atmosphere to take in the surrounding views
- Inside, the expansive living/dining area is completely open to the kitchen for ideal entertaining
- The master bedroom conveniently houses two closets
- 2 bedrooms, 1 bath
- Basement foundation

Large Loft Area Offers Endless Possibilities

- 1,426 total square feet of living area
- Energy efficient home with 2" x 6" exterior walls
- Large front deck invites outdoor relaxation
- Expansive windows, skylights, vaulted ceiling and fireplace enhance the living and dining room combination
- Nook, adjacent to the living room, has a cozy window seat
- Kitchen is open to the living and dining rooms
- 1 bedroom, 1 bath
- Crawl space foundation

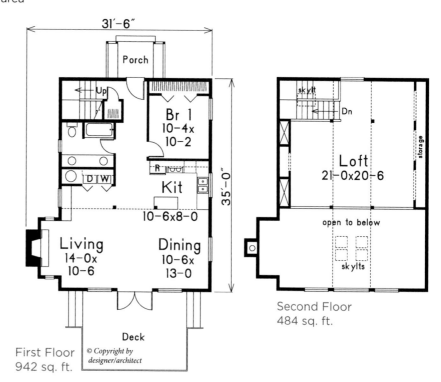

First Floor
942 sq. ft.

© Copyright by designer/architect

Second Floor
484 sq. ft.

Formal And Informal Gathering Rooms

- 1,314 total square feet of living area
- U-shaped kitchen joins the cozy dining area
- The family room has direct access into the garage
- Roomy closets serve the second floor bedrooms
- 3 bedrooms, 1 1/2 baths, 2-car garage
- Basement foundation, drawings also include crawl space foundation

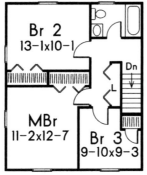

Br 2
13-1x10-1

Dn

MBr
11-2x12-7

Br 3
9-10x9-3

Second Floor
552 sq. ft.

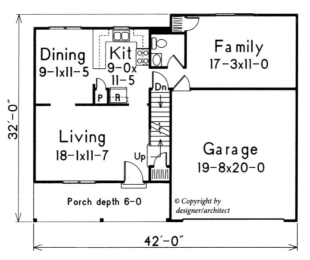

Dining
9-1x11-5

Kit
9-0x
11-5

Family
17-3x11-0

Dn

Living
18-1x11-7

Up

Garage
19-8x20-0

32'-0"

Porch depth 6-0

© Copyright by
designer/architect

First Floor
762 sq. ft.

42'-0"

Compact Ranch Is An Ideal Starter Home

- 988 total square feet of living area
- Great room features a corner fireplace
- Vaulted ceiling and corner windows add space and light to the great room
- Eat-in kitchen with vaulted ceiling accesses deck for outdoor living
- Master bedroom features separate vanities and private access to the bath
- 2 bedrooms, 1 bath, 2-car garage
- Basement foundation

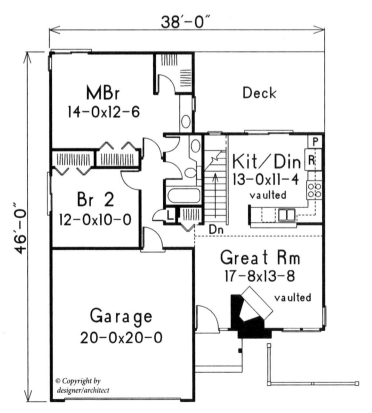

Small Ranch With Three-Car Garage And Covered Deck

- 1,348 total square feet of living area
- Ideal retirement home or lakeside retreat with a country flavor
- The living room has a corner stone fireplace and carefully planned shelving for a flat panel TV and components
- A luxury bath, huge walk-in closet and covered deck adjoin the master bedroom
- The lower level is comprised of a guest bedroom, hall bath and garage with space for two cars and a boat
- 2 bedrooms, 2 1/2 baths, 3-car rear entry garage
- Walk-out basement foundation

45'-4"

Covered Deck

Living Rm
14-3x16-9

Dining
9-4x9-4

MBr
12-0x15-4

shelves

Kit
9-4x
14-0

DW

Entry

Dn

29'-0"

Porch

First Floor
1,008 sq. ft.

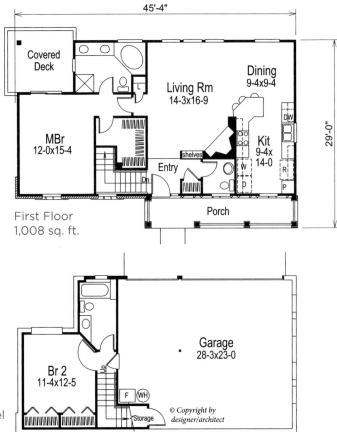

Br 2
11-4x12-5

Garage
28-3x23-0

F WH

Storage

© Copyright by
designer/architect

Lower Level
340 sq. ft.

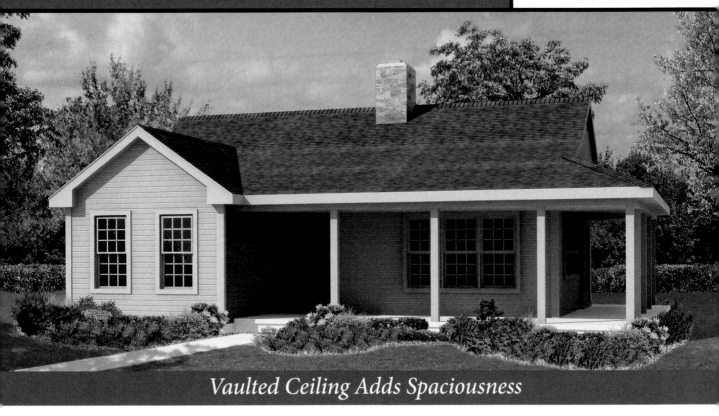

Vaulted Ceiling Adds Spaciousness

- 990 total square feet of living area
- Wrap-around porch creates a relaxing retreat
- Combined family and dining rooms boast vaulted ceilings
- Space for an efficiency washer and dryer unit offers convenience
- 2" x 6" exterior walls available, please order plan #539-058D-0086
- 2 bedrooms, 1 bath
- Crawl space foundation

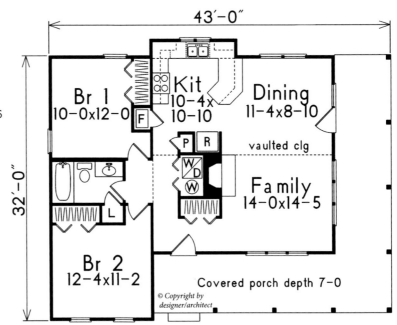

Affordable Four Bedroom Ranch

- 1,203 total square feet of living area
- Large porch for quiet evening relaxation
- The living room features a vaulted ceiling, fireplace and dining area with patio views
- The kitchen includes an abundance of cabinet storage, a large walk-in pantry and door to the rear yard
- The master bedroom has a vaulted ceiling, private bath with built-in linen storage and a walk-in closet
- 4 bedrooms, 2 1/2 baths, 2-car garage
- Basement foundation, drawings also include slab and crawl space foundations

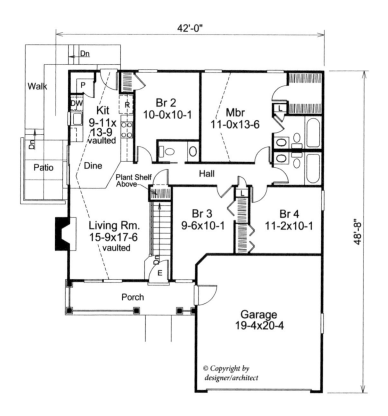

Large Front Porch Adds Welcoming Appeal

- 829 total square feet of living area
- U-shaped kitchen opens into living area by a 42" high counter
- An oversized bay window and access to the backyard accent the dining room
- Gathering space is created by the large living room
- Convenient utility room and linen closet
- 1 bedroom, 1 bath
- Slab foundation

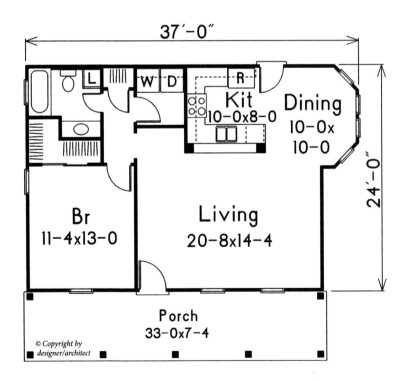

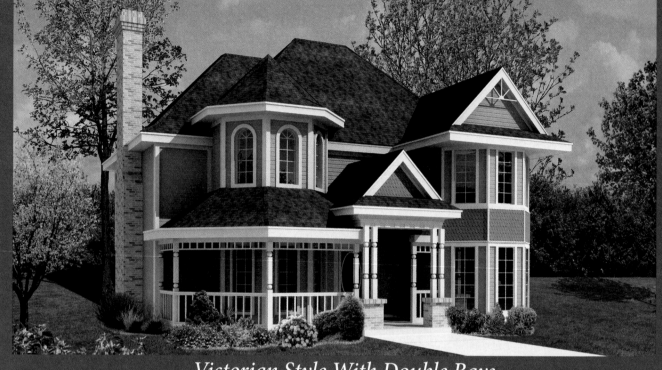

Victorian Style With Double Bays

- 2,066 total square feet of living area
- Large master bedroom includes a sitting area and private bath
- Open living room features a fireplace with built-in bookshelves
- Spacious kitchen accesses formal dining area and breakfast area
- 3 bedrooms, 2 1/2 baths, optional 2-car side entry garage
- Slab foundation

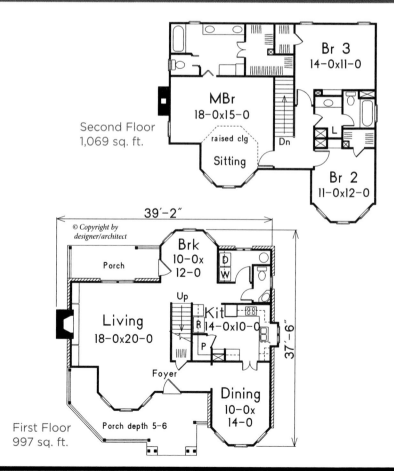

Second Floor
1,069 sq. ft.

Br 3
14-0x11-0

MBr
18-0x15-0

raised clg

Sitting

Dn

Br 2
11-0x12-0

39'-2"

© Copyright by
designer/architect

Brk
10-0x
12-0

Porch

Up

Kit
14-0x10-0

Living
18-0x20-0

Foyer

37'-6"

Dining
10-0x
14-0

First Floor
997 sq. ft.

Porch depth 5-6

To Order See Page 254 or Call Toll-Free 1-877-379-3420

Openness Reflects Relaxed Lifestyle

- 1,330 total square feet of living area
- The vaulted living room is open to the bayed dining area and kitchen creating an ideal space for entertaining
- Two bedrooms, a linen closet and bath complete the first floor and are easily accessible
- The second floor offers two bedrooms with walk-in closets, a very large storage area and an opening with louvered doors which overlooks the living room
- 4 bedrooms, 2 baths, 1-car garage
- Basement foundation

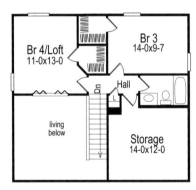

Second Floor
446 sq. ft.

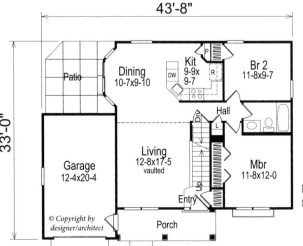

First Floor
884 sq. ft.

Charming Country Home

- 1,751 total square feet of living area
- A wide front porch and decorative window above the entry adds a country flavor to this home
- The kitchen enjoys an abundance of counterspace and includes an island that opens to the spacious dining room
- The master bedroom is privately located on the first floor while two additional bedrooms are located on the second floor
- 3 bedrooms, 2 baths, 2-car detached garage
- Basement foundation

Second Floor
561 sq. ft.

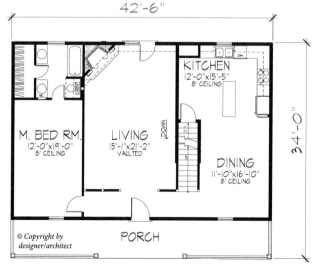

First Floor
1,190 sq. ft.

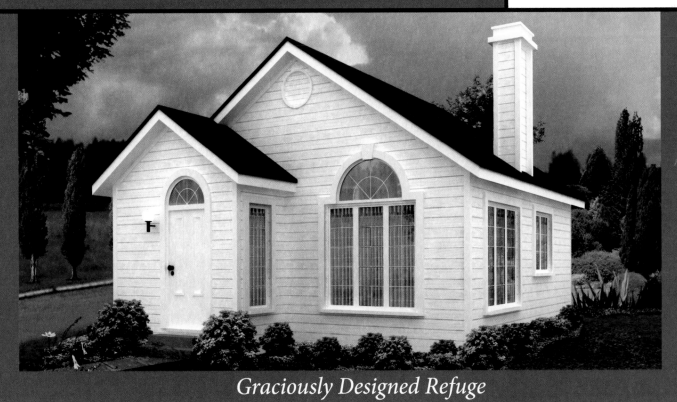

Graciously Designed Refuge

- 527 total square feet of living area
- Cleverly arranged home has it all
- Foyer spills into the dining nook with access to side views
- An excellent kitchen offers a long breakfast bar and borders the living room with a free-standing fireplace
- A cozy bedroom has a full bath just across the hall
- 1 bedroom, 1 bath
- Crawl space foundation

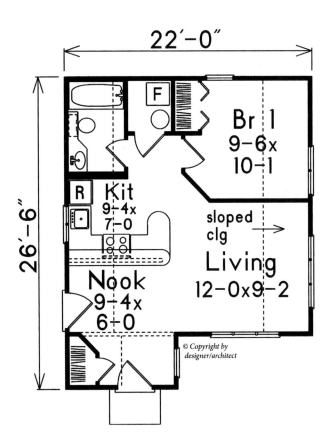

Especially Designed For A Small Lot

- 1,137 total square feet of living area

- Cleverly designed two-story is disguised as an attractive one-story home

- The spacious and dramatic entry features a vaulted ceiling, coat closet with plant shelf above and an ascending stair to the second floor

- The living room with fireplace is open to the bayed dining area and functional L-shaped kitchen furnished with an island counter and adjacent laundry room

- The optional finished lower level includes a family room, hall bath and third bedroom with walk-in closet and allows for an extra 591 square feet of living area

- 2 bedrooms, 1 1/2 baths, 2-car garage

- Walk-out basement foundation

First Floor
621 sq. ft.

Second Floor
516 sq. ft.

Optional
Lower Level

© Copyright by designer/architect

LOWE'S
LEGACY
SERIES

Terrific Lake House For A Tight Budget

- 1,694 total square feet of living area
- The vaulted great room, dining and kitchen borrow space and natural light from the atrium to create spacious living in a small home
- A vaulted ceiling, double entry doors, luxurious bath and large walk-in closet are features of the master bedroom that are rarely found in a home of this size
- The lower level consists of a family room/atrium, two secondary bedrooms, a full bath, mechanical closet/laundry and a two-car rear entry garage perfect for boat storage and lake access
- 3 bedrooms, 2 1/2 baths, 2-car drive under rear entry garage
- Walk-out basement foundation

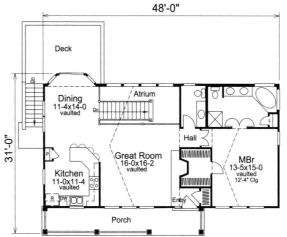

First Floor
1,094 sq. ft.

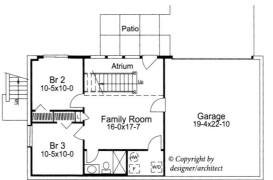

Lower Level
600 sq. ft.

Practical Two-Story, Full Of Features

- 2,058 total square feet of living area
- Handsome two-story foyer with balcony creates a spacious entrance area
- Vaulted master bedroom has a private dressing area and large walk-in closet
- Skylights furnish natural lighting in the hall and master bath
- The laundry closet is conveniently located on the second floor near the bedrooms
- 3 bedrooms, 2 1/2 baths, 2-car garage
- Basement foundation, drawings also include slab and crawl space foundations

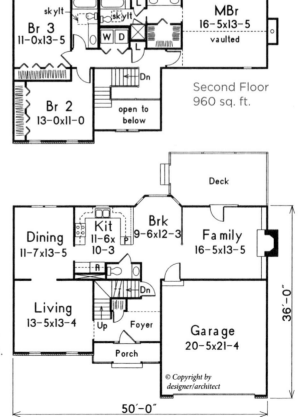

Br 3
11-0x13-5

MBr
16-5x13-5
vaulted

Br 2
13-0x11-0

open to below

Second Floor
960 sq. ft.

Deck

Dining
11-7x13-5

Kit
11-6x
10-3

Brk
9-6x12-3

Family
16-5x13-5

Living
13-5x13-4

Foyer

Garage
20-5x21-4

Porch

36'-0"

50'-0"

First Floor
1,098 sq. ft.

© Copyright by designer/architect

To Order See Page 254 or Call Toll-Free 1-877-379-3420

Narrow Lot Living

- 1,941 total square feet of living area
- This home is designed to easily fit a narrow lot with its side entry
- A corner window brightens the vaulted living room and adds style to the exterior
- Bay windows accent the master bedroom and breakfast room, adding elegance and natural light
- 3 bedrooms, 2 1/2 baths, 2-car garage
- Basement foundation

40'-0"

DECK
14/0X12/0

BRKFST
10/0X6/6

KIT
16/3X11/9
9 clg

M. BR.
12/9X15/9
9 clg

DINING
14/10X12/1
9 clg

ENTRY

LIVING
18/9X12/1
15 vaulted clg

69'-8"

GARAGE
20/5X19/9

© Copyright by
designer/architect

First Floor
1,494 sq. ft.

BR. #2
13/5X12/5

BR. #3
11/6X10/5

Second Floor
447 sq. ft.

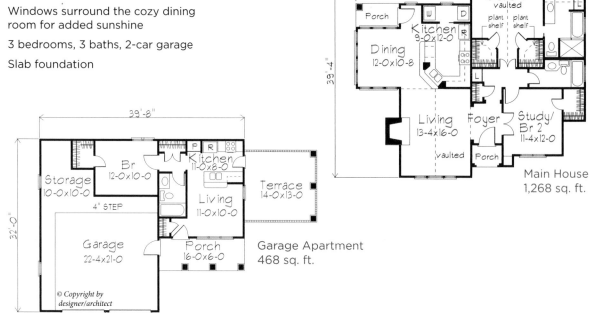

Ranch Layout Has Two Separate Living Quarters

- 1,736 total square feet of living area
- Vaulted master bedroom features a double-door entry and private bath
- Garage apartment comes complete with adjacent terrace and porch
- Windows surround the cozy dining room for added sunshine
- 3 bedrooms, 3 baths, 2-car garage
- Slab foundation

Main House
1,268 sq. ft.

Garage Apartment
468 sq. ft.

© Copyright by designer/architect

English Cottage With Modern Amenities

- 1,816 total square feet of living area
- The living room features a two-way fireplace with nearby window seat
- Wrap-around dining room windows create a sunroom appearance
- Master bedroom has abundant closet and storage space
- Rear dormers, closets and desk areas create an interesting and functional second floor
- 3 bedrooms, 2 1/2 baths, 2-car detached garage
- Slab foundation, drawings also include crawl space foundation

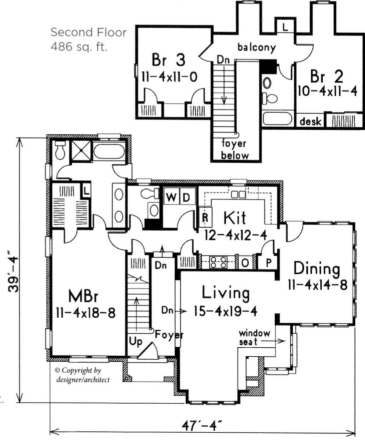

Second Floor
486 sq. ft.

Br 3
11-4x11-0

balcony

Dn

Br 2
10-4x11-4

desk

foyer
below

First Floor
1,330 sq. ft.

39'-4"

47'-4"

W D

R

Kit
12-4x12-4

O   P

Dining
11-4x14-8

Dn

MBr
11-4x18-8

Dn

Living
15-4x19-4

Up   Foyer

window
seat

© *Copyright by designer/architect*

Floor-To-Ceiling Window Expands Compact Two-Story

- 1,246 total square feet of living area
- Corner living room window adds openness and light
- Out-of-the-way kitchen with dining area accesses the outdoors
- Private first floor master bedroom has interesting corner windows
- Large walk-in closet is located in bedroom #3
- Easily built perimeter allows economical construction
- 3 bedrooms, 2 baths, 2-car garage
- Basement foundation

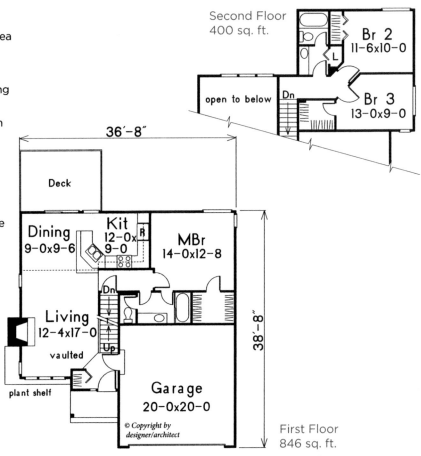

© Copyright by designer/architect

Tudor Accents Add A Lot Of Curb Appeal

- 2,169 total square feet of living area

- Breakfast nook, keeping room and kitchen flow together for great function and design perfect for the whole family

- A gallery style entry into the formal dining room offers a nice element of surprise and drama to the space

- The exceptional master bath has double walk-in closets keeping everything easily organized

- 3 bedrooms, 2 baths, 2-car rear entry garage

- Slab foundation

Compact Home, Perfect Fit For Narrow Lot

- 1,085 total square feet of living area
- Rear porch provides handy access through the kitchen
- Convenient hall linen closet is located on the second floor
- Breakfast bar in the kitchen offers additional counterspace
- Living and dining rooms combine for open living
- 3 bedrooms, 2 baths
- Basement foundation

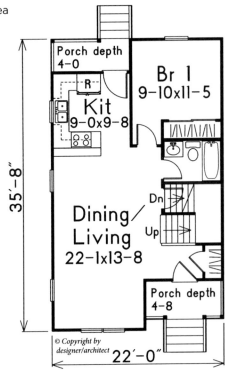

First Floor
685 sq. ft.

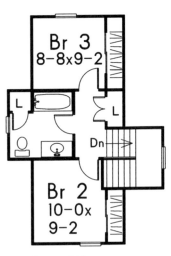

Second Floor
400 sq. ft.

Small And Cozy Cabin

- 676 total square feet of living area

- See-through fireplace between bedroom and living area adds character

- Combined dining and living areas create an open feeling

- Full-length front covered porch is perfect for enjoying the outdoors

- Additional storage is available in the utility room

- 2" x 6" exterior walls available, please order plan #539-058D-0074

- 1 bedroom, 1 bath

- Crawl space foundation

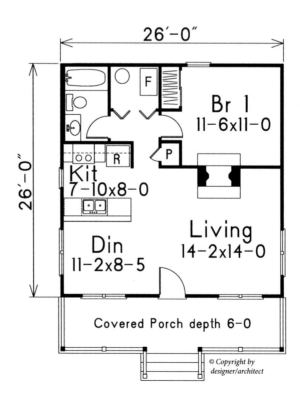

Br 1
11-6x11-0

Kit
7-10x8-0

Din
11-2x8-5

Living
14-2x14-0

26'-0"

26'-0"

Covered Porch depth 6-0

© Copyright by designer/architect

Spacious Dining And Living Areas

- 1,104 total square feet of living area
- Master bedroom includes a private bath
- Convenient side entrance to the dining area/kitchen
- Laundry area is located near the kitchen
- Large living area creates a comfortable atmosphere
- 3 bedrooms, 2 baths
- Crawl space foundation, drawings also slab foundation

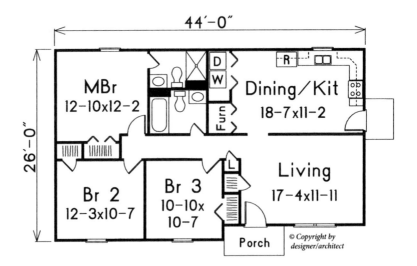

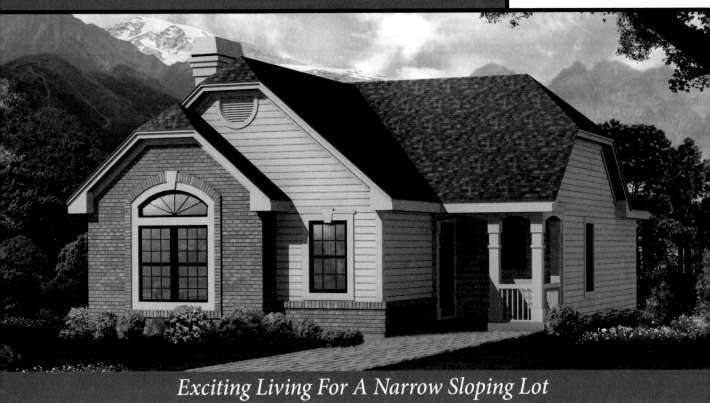

Exciting Living For A Narrow Sloping Lot

- 1,200 total square feet of living area
- Entry leads to a large dining area that opens to the kitchen and sun-drenched living room
- An expansive window wall in the two-story atrium lends space and light to the living room with fireplace
- The large kitchen features a breakfast bar, built-in pantry and storage galore
- 697 square feet of optional living area on the lower level includes a family room, bedroom #3 and a bath
- 2 bedrooms, 1 bath
- Walk-out basement foundation

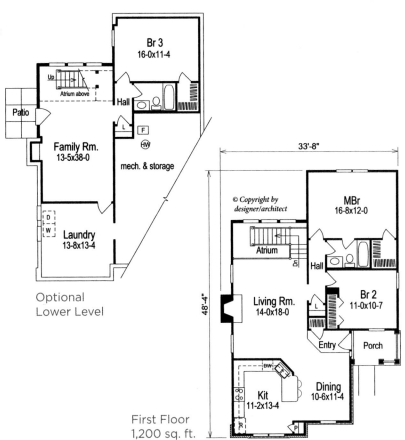

Optional
Lower Level

First Floor
1,200 sq. ft.

Unique Design With Large Rear Deck

- 1,836 total square feet of living area
- Foyer sparkles with spiral stairs, a sloped ceiling and celestial windows
- Living room enjoys a fireplace with bookshelves and a view to the outdoors
- U-shaped kitchen includes an eat-in breakfast area and dining nearby
- Master bedroom revels in having a balcony overlooking the living room, a large walk-in closet and private bath
- 3 bedrooms, 2 1/2 baths
- Crawl space foundation, drawings also include slab foundation

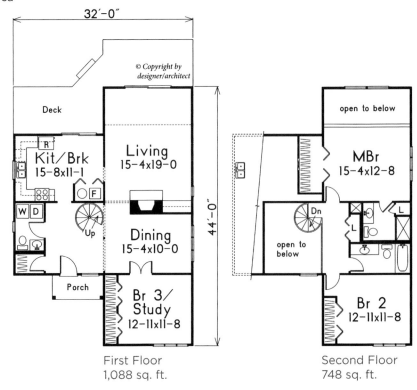

First Floor
1,088 sq. ft.

Second Floor
748 sq. ft.

Country Charm For A Small Lot

- 1,169 total square feet of living area
- Front facade features a distinctive country appeal
- Living room enjoys a wood-burning fireplace and pass-through to the kitchen
- A stylish U-shaped kitchen offers an abundance of cabinet and counterspace with a view to the living room
- A large walk-in closet, access to the rear patio and a private bath are some of the many features of the master bedroom
- 3 bedrooms, 2 baths, 1-car garage
- Basement foundation

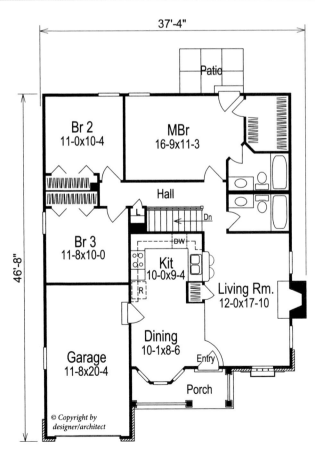

37'-4"

46'-8"

Patio

Br 2
11-0x10-4

MBr
16-9x11-3

Hall

Br 3
11-8x10-0

Dn

DW

Kit
10-0x9-4

R

Living Rm.
12-0x17-10

Dining
10-1x8-6

Entry

Garage
11-8x20-4

Porch

© Copyright by designer/architect

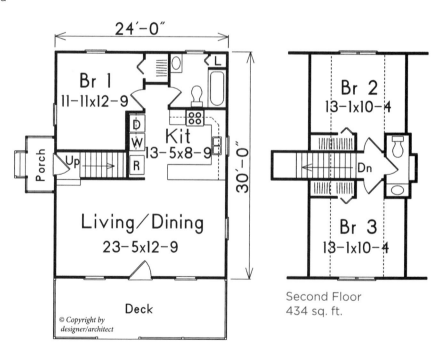

Open Living Area

- 1,154 total square feet of living area
- U-shaped kitchen features a large breakfast bar and handy laundry area
- Private second floor bedrooms share a half bath
- Large living/dining area opens to the deck
- 3 bedrooms, 1 1/2 baths
- Crawl space foundation, drawings also include slab foundation

24'-0"

30'-0"

Br 1
11-11x12-9

Porch

Up

D
W
R

Kit
13-5x8-9

L

Living/Dining
23-5x12-9

© Copyright by designer/architect

Deck

First Floor
720 sq. ft.

Br 2
13-1x10-4

Dn

Br 3
13-1x10-4

Second Floor
434 sq. ft.

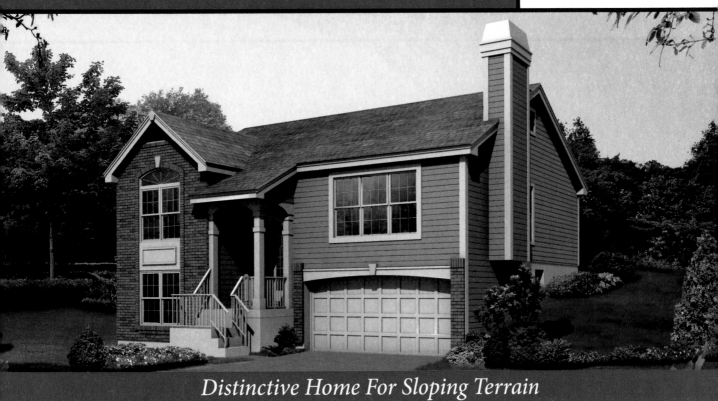

Distinctive Home For Sloping Terrain

- 1,340 total square feet of living area
- Grand-sized vaulted living and dining rooms offer a fireplace, wet bar and breakfast counter open to a spacious kitchen
- Vaulted master bedroom features a double-door entry, walk-in closet and an elegant bath
- Basement includes a huge two-car garage and space for a bedroom/bath expansion
- Optional lower level has an additional 636 square feet of living area
- 3 bedrooms, 2 baths, 2-car drive under garage with storage area
- Basement foundation

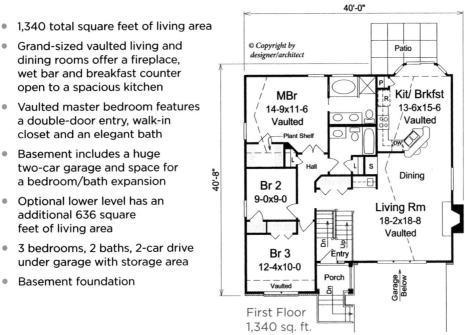

First Floor
1,340 sq. ft.

Optional
Lower Level

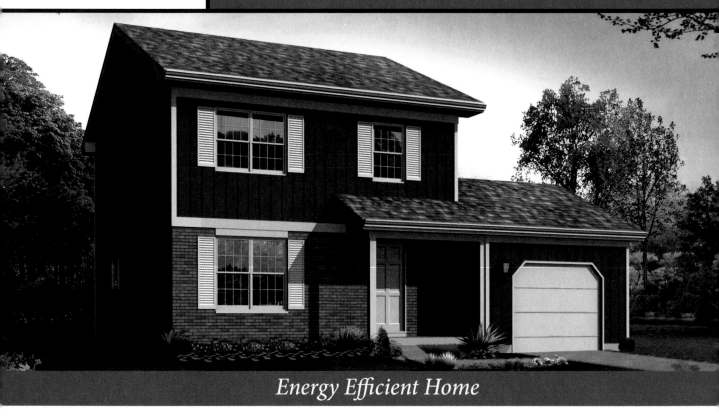

Energy Efficient Home

- 1,536 total square feet of living area
- Formal living room featured in the front of the home
- Combined living areas create the back of the home with great room, dining area and kitchen all in one
- Second floor master bedroom includes a private bath
- 3 bedrooms, 2 1/2 baths, 1-car garage
- Basement foundation, drawings also include crawl space and slab foundations

One Car 37'-8"
Two Car 45'-8"

Dining
10-8x7-6

Great Rm
12-8x12-11

Kit
10-8x8-0

Living Rm
11-7x15-1

Foyer

Garage
13-4x21-4

Two Car

36'-0"

Porch

© *Copyright by designer/architect*

First Floor
768 sq. ft.

Bedrm 2
11-7x11-1

Bedrm 3
11-6x10-1

Mstr Bedrm
11-7x15-3

Second Floor
768 sq. ft.

Gables Accent This Home

- 1,239 total square feet of living area
- Master bedroom has a private bath and walk-in closet
- Convenient coat closet and pantry are located near the garage entrance
- Dining area accesses the deck
- Stairway with sloped ceiling creates an open atmosphere in the great room
- 3 bedrooms, 2 1/2 baths, 2-car garage
- Basement foundation

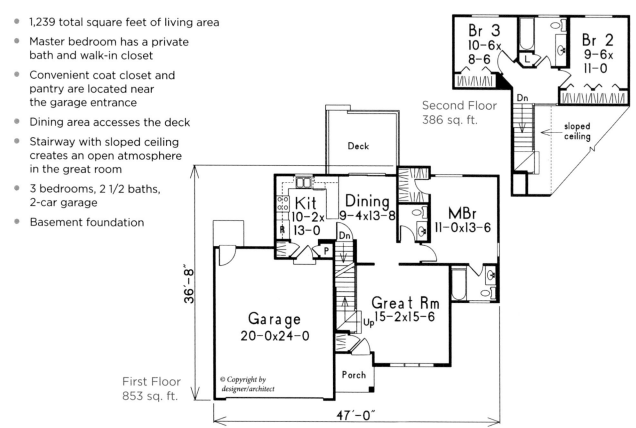

Trendsetting Appeal For A Narrow Lot

- 1,294 total square feet of living area
- Great room features a fireplace and large bay with windows and a patio door
- Enjoy a laundry room immersed in light with large windows, an arched transom and attractive planter box
- Vaulted master bedroom features a bay window and two walk-in closets
- The studio/bedroom #2 boasts a vaulted ceiling, plant shelf and half bath, perfect for a studio
- 2 bedrooms, 1 full bath, 2 half baths, 1-car rear entry garage
- Basement foundation

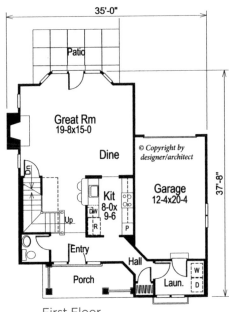

First Floor
718 sq. ft.

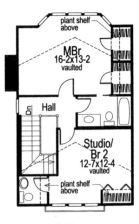

Second Floor
576 sq. ft.

LOWE'S
LEGACY
SERIES

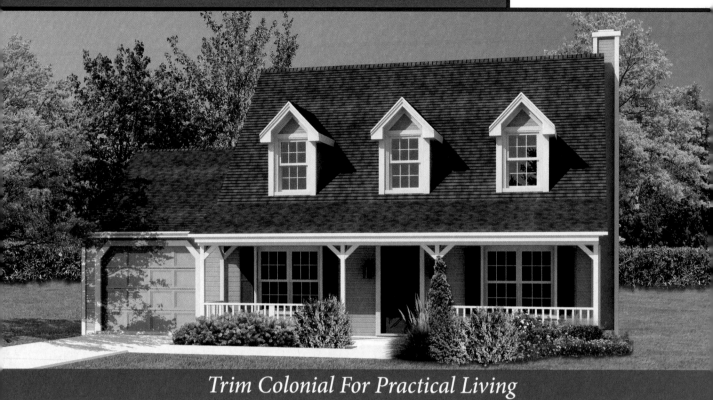

Trim Colonial For Practical Living

- 1,582 total square feet of living area
- Conservative layout gives privacy to the living and dining rooms
- Large fireplace and windows enhance the living room
- Rear door in garage is convenient to the garden and kitchen
- Full front porch adds charm
- Dormers add light to the foyer and bedrooms
- 3 bedrooms, 2 1/2 baths, 1-car garage
- Slab foundation, drawings also include crawl space foundation

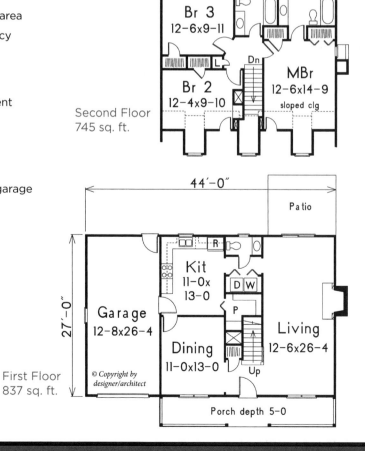

Br 3
12-6x9-11

Br 2
12-4x9-10

MBr
12-6x14-9
sloped clg

Dn

Second Floor
745 sq. ft.

44'-0"

Patio

Kit
11-0x 13-0

Garage
12-8x26-4

27'-0"

Dining
11-0x13-0

Living
12-6x26-4

Up

© Copyright by
designer/architect

First Floor
837 sq. ft.

Porch depth 5-0

Energy Efficient Two-Story Berm Home

- 1,105 total square feet of living area

- Energy efficient home with 2" x 6" exterior walls

- This fresh, modern design enjoys sleek window lines and a stucco exterior making it truly a one-of-a-kind living experience

- The compact, yet efficient U-shaped kitchen offers a tremendous amount of counterspace within reach for all sort of kitchen tasks at hand

- A tall sloped ceiling in the two-story living room gives this home an open and spacious feel all those who enter will appreciate

- 2 bedrooms, 1 1/2 baths

- Slab foundation

First Floor
880 sq. ft.

Second Floor
225 sq. ft.

Lowe's
LEGACY
SERIES

Little Cottage With Big Spaces

- 771 total square feet of living area

- The living room includes a vaulted ceiling, separate entry with guest closet and glass doors to the rear deck

- A vaulted ceiling and overhead plant shelf are two attractive features of the L-shaped kitchen

- The lower level is comprised of a spacious bedroom complete with a private bath, walk-in closet and glass doors to the rear patio

- 1 bedroom, 1 1/2 baths, 1-car side entry garage

- Walk-out basement foundation

Patio

Mech.

F

Bedroom
13-4x14-6

UP

Lower Level
358 sq. ft.

26'-4"

Deck

DN

Living Room
14-0x12-8
Vaulted

Kitchen
11-9x7-10
Vaulted

DW   R

Entry

28'-0"

Garage
21-4x12-0

© Copyright by
designer/architect

First Floor
413 sq. ft.

Old World Charm For A Narrow Lot

- 2,250 total square feet of living area
- The spacious living room with fireplace enjoys an adjacent entry foyer, guest closet and large separate dining area with access to the rear patio
- A snack bar, center island and walk-in pantry are a few amenities of the well-designed kitchen
- The breakfast area, open to the kitchen, has an interesting curved wall and glass sliding doors to the rear patio
- All second floor bedrooms are generous in size including the vaulted master suite with walk-in closet and luxury bath
- Finished lower level has 134 square feet of living area that is included in the total square footage
- 3 bedrooms, 2 1/2 baths, 2-car garage
- Basement foundation

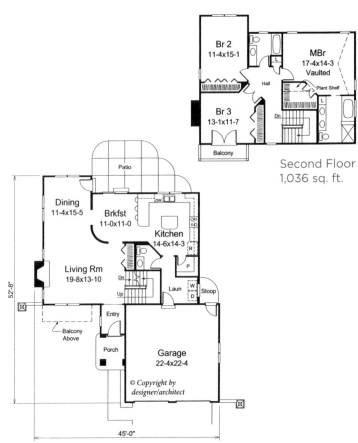

Second Floor
1,036 sq. ft.

First Floor
1,080 sq. ft.

Perfect For A Narrow Lot

- 1,548 total square feet of living area
- The garage enters the home through a laundry area into the breakfast room for easy unloading
- The formal dining room offers an enchanting atmosphere with the surrounding windows
- Both bedrooms enjoy private baths
- 2 bedrooms, 2 baths, 2-car rear entry garage
- Basement foundation, drawings also include slab foundation

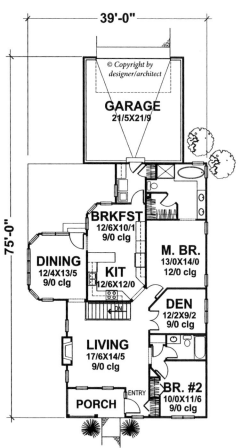

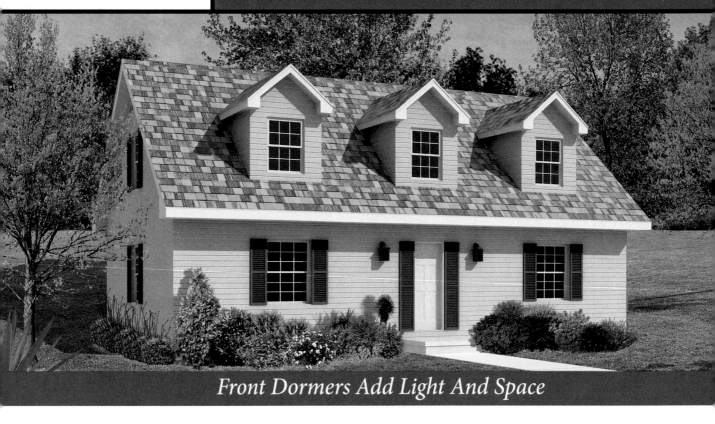

Front Dormers Add Light And Space

- 1,705 total square feet of living area
- Cozy design includes two bedrooms on the first floor and two bedrooms on the second floor for added privacy
- L-shaped kitchen provides easy access to the dining room and the outdoors
- Convenient first floor laundry area
- 2" x 6" exterior walls available, please order plan #539-001D-0111
- 4 bedrooms, 2 baths
- Crawl space foundation, drawings also include basement and slab foundations

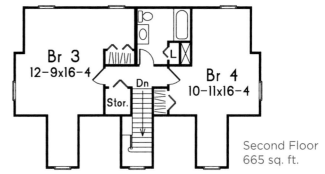

Second Floor
665 sq. ft.

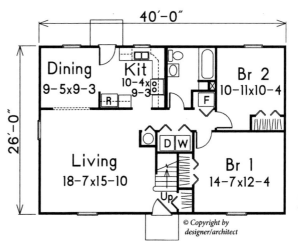

First Floor
1,040 sq. ft.

© Copyright by
designer/architect

Country Two-Story With Built-In Screened Porch

- 2,050 total square feet of living area

- Large living room with fireplace enjoys a view to the front porch and access to the rear screened porch

- L-shaped kitchen has a built-in pantry, island snack bar and breakfast area with bay window

- Master bedroom is vaulted and has a luxury bath with abundant closet space

- The spacious secondary bedrooms each have a walk-in closet

- 3 bedrooms, 2 1/2 baths, 2-car detached garage

- Basement foundation, drawings also include slab and crawl space foundations

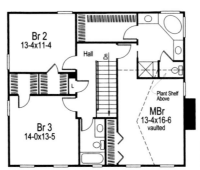

Second Floor
1,080 sq. ft.

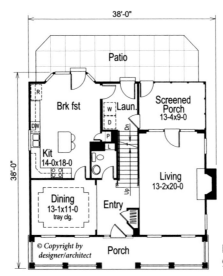

First Floor
970 sq. ft.

Great Design For Vacation Home Or Year-Round Living

- 990 total square feet of living area
- Covered front porch adds a charming feel
- Vaulted ceilings in the kitchen, family and dining rooms create a spacious feel
- Large linen, pantry and storage closets throughout
- 2 bedrooms, 1 bath
- Crawl space foundation

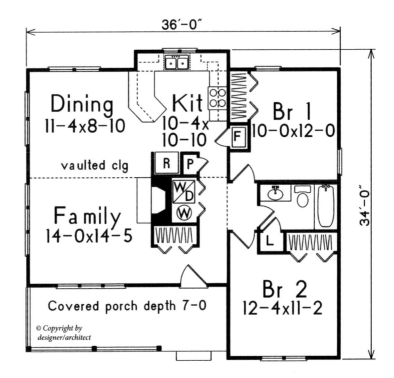

36'-0"

Dining
11-4x8-10

Kit
10-4x
10-10

Br 1
10-0x12-0

vaulted clg

R P

W/D

W

Family
14-0x14-5

L

Br 2
12-4x11-2

34'-0"

Covered porch depth 7-0

© Copyright by
designer/architect

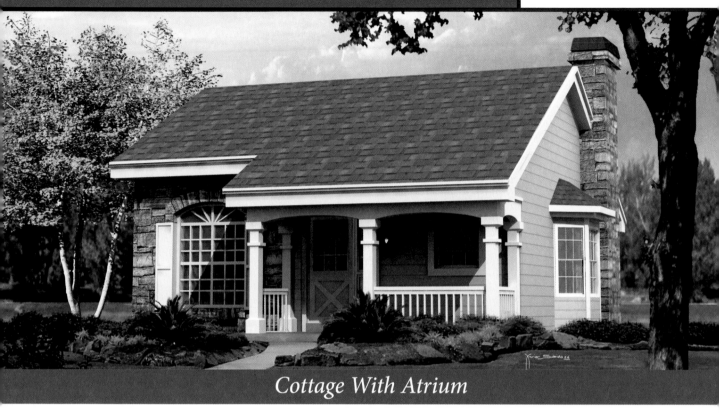

Cottage With Atrium

- 969 total square feet of living area

- Eye-pleasing facade enjoys stone accents along with a country porch for quiet evenings

- A bayed dining area, cozy fireplace and atrium with sunny two-story windows are the many features of the living room

- Step-saver kitchen includes a pass-through snack bar

- 325 square feet of optional living area on the lower level

- 2 bedrooms, 1 bath, 1-car rear entry drive under garage

- Walk-out basement foundation

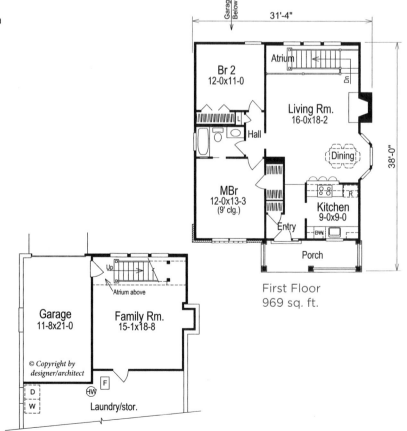

First Floor
969 sq. ft.

Optional
Lower Level

Front Porch Adds Style To This Ranch

- 1,496 total square feet of living area

- Master bedroom features a tray ceiling, walk-in closet and spacious bath

- Vaulted ceiling and fireplace grace the family room

- Dining room is adjacent to the kitchen and features access to the rear porch

- Convenient access to the utility room from the kitchen

- 3 bedrooms, 2 baths, 2-car drive under garage

- Basement foundation

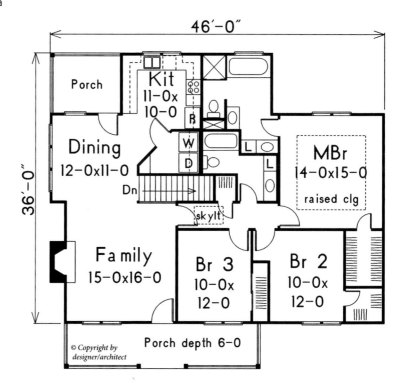

46'-0"

36'-0"

Porch

Kit 11-0x 10-0

Dining 12-0x11-0

Dn

sky lt

MBr 14-0x15-0

raised clg

Family 15-0x16-0

Br 3 10-0x 12-0

Br 2 10-0x 12-0

© Copyright by designer/architect

Porch depth 6-0

Innovative Ranch Has Cozy Corner Patio

- 1,092 total square feet of living area
- A box window and inviting porch with dormers create a charming facade
- Eat-in kitchen offers a pass-through breakfast bar, corner window wall to patio, pantry and convenient laundry room with half bath
- Master bedroom features a double-door entry and walk-in closet
- 3 bedrooms, 1 1/2 baths, 1-car garage
- Basement foundation, drawings also include slab and crawl space foundations

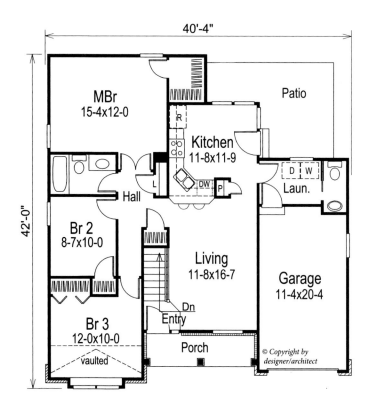

Irresistible Paradise Retreat

- 1,563 total square feet of living area
- Enjoyable wrap-around porch and lower sundeck
- Vaulted entry is adorned with a palladian window, plant shelves, stone floor and fireplace
- Huge vaulted great room has a magnificent view through a two-story atrium window wall
- 2 bedrooms, 1 1/2 baths
- Walk-out basement foundation

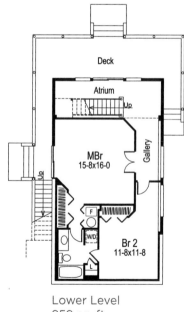

Lower Level
858 sq. ft.

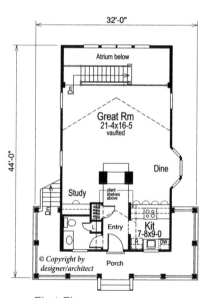

First Floor
705 sq. ft.

Open Great Room

- 1,550 total square feet of living area
- Greenhouse windows in the kitchen create the perfect place to grow herbs or vegetables
- The sunken great room has a cozy corner fireplace and a vaulted ceiling
- The second floor includes a large loft area that could make an excellent place for a home office
- 2 bedrooms, 2 1/2 baths, 2-car garage
- Basement foundation

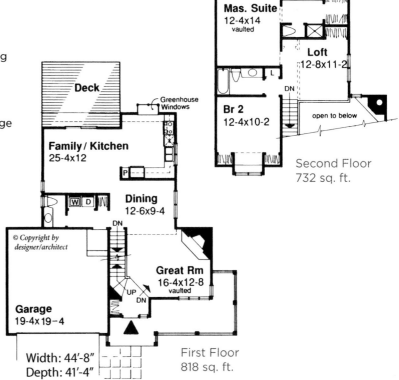

Mas. Suite
12-4x14
vaulted

Loft
12-8x11-2

Br 2
12-4x10-2

open to below

Second Floor
732 sq. ft.

Deck

Greenhouse Windows

Family / Kitchen
25-4x12

Dining
12-6x9-4

P

W D

DN

© Copyright by designer/architect

UP
DN

Great Rm
16-4x12-8
vaulted

Garage
19-4x 19–4

Width: 44'-8"
Depth: 41'-4"

First Floor
818 sq. ft.

Plan #539-007D-0179 • **Price Code AA**

Versatile Cottage Has Many Uses

- 1,131 total square feet of living area
- Inviting porch and roof dormer create a charming exterior
- The spacious area on the first floor is perfect for a large shop, private studio, office or cottage great room and includes a fireplace, kitchenette and half bath
- Two bedrooms, a full bath and attic storage comprise the second floor which has its own private entrance and wide sunny hallway
- 2 bedrooms, 1 1/2 baths
- Slab foundation

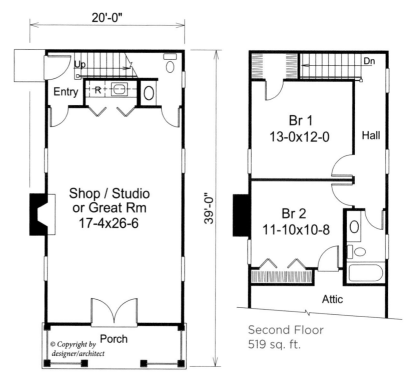

20'-0"

Up

Entry R

Shop / Studio or Great Rm
17-4x26-6

39'-0"

© Copyright by designer/architect

Porch

First Floor
612 sq. ft.

Dn

Br 1
13-0x12-0

Hall

Br 2
11-10x10-8

Attic

Second Floor
519 sq. ft.

Compact Home With Functional Design

- 1,396 total square feet of living area
- Gabled front adds interest to the facade
- Living and dining rooms share a vaulted ceiling
- Master bedroom features a walk-in closet and private bath
- Functional kitchen boasts a center work island and convenient pantry
- 3 bedrooms, 2 baths, 1-car rear entry carport
- Basement foundation, drawings also include crawl space foundation

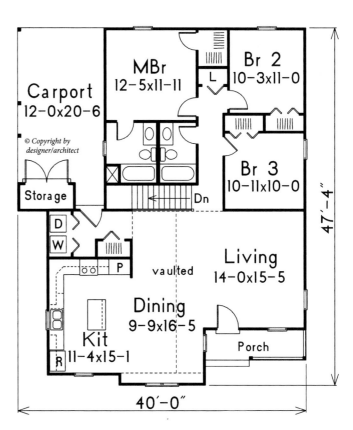

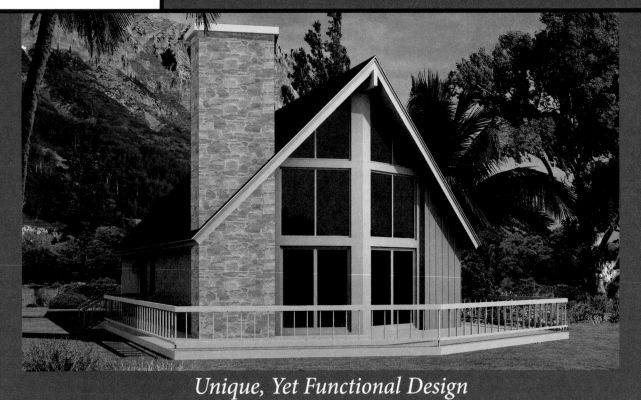

Unique, Yet Functional Design

- 1,316 total square feet of living area
- Massive vaulted family/living room is accented with a fireplace and views to the outdoors through sliding glass doors
- Galley-style kitchen is centrally located
- Unique separate shower room near bath doubles as a convenient mud room
- 3 bedrooms, 1 bath
- Crawl space foundation

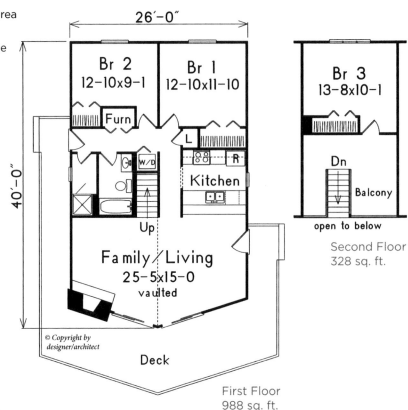

26'-0"

40'-0"

Br 2
12-10x9-1

Br 1
12-10x11-10

Furn

W/D

Kitchen

Up

Family/Living
25-5x15-0
vaulted

© Copyright by
designer/architect

Deck

First Floor
988 sq. ft.

Br 3
13-8x10-1

Dn

Balcony

open to below

Second Floor
328 sq. ft.

Gracious Living On A Small Lot

- 1,671 total square feet of living area
- Triple gables and a stone facade create great curb appeal
- Two-story entry with hallway leads to a spacious family room, dining area with bay window and U-shaped kitchen
- Second floor features a large master bedroom with luxury bath, huge walk-in closet, overlook to entry and two secondary bedrooms with hall bath
- 3 bedrooms, 2 1/2 baths, 2-car garage
- Basement foundation

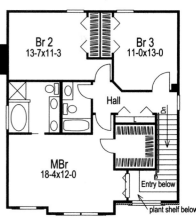

Second Floor
991 sq. ft.

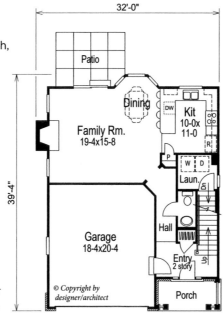

First Floor
680 sq. ft.

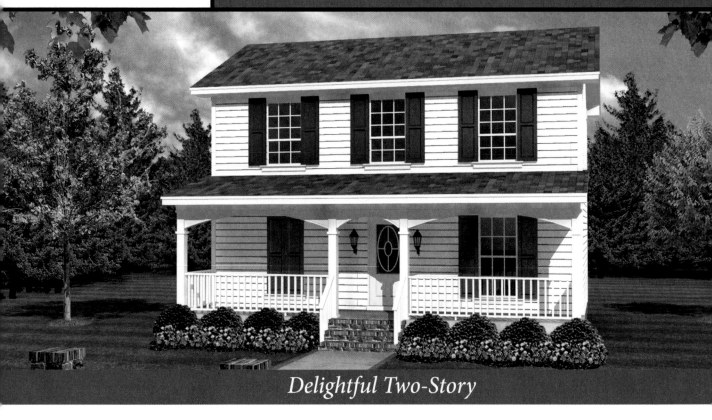

Delightful Two-Story

- 1,200 total square feet of living area
- Enjoy the open living area made possible with the raised snack bar connecting the kitchen to the living room
- Front and rear porches provide lovely settings for relaxing in the great outdoors
- Each bedroom features a walk-in closet for easy organization
- Designed with insulated concrete formed exterior walls providing a tighter construction, conserving heating and cooling energy consumption
- 3 bedrooms, 2 baths
- Slab foundation, drawings also include crawl space foundation

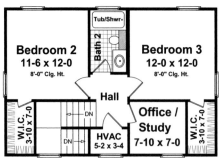

Second Floor
600 sq. ft.

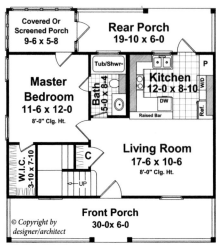

First Floor
600 sq. ft.

Width: 30'-0"
Depth: 32'-0"

Two-Story Home Is A Perfect Fit For A Small Lot

- 858 total square feet of living area
- Stackable washer/dryer is located in the kitchen
- Large covered porch graces this exterior
- Both bedrooms have walk-in closets
- 2 bedrooms, 1 bath
- Crawl space foundation

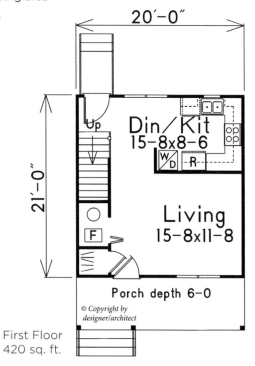

20'-0"

21'-0"

Up

Din/Kit
15-8x8-6

W/D R

Living
15-8x11-8

F

Porch depth 6-0

© Copyright by
designer/architect

First Floor
420 sq. ft.

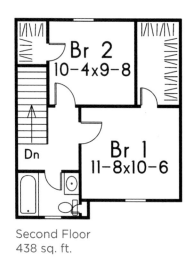

Br 2
10-4x9-8

Dn

Br 1
11-8x10-6

Second Floor
438 sq. ft.

Functional Livability In A Small Ranch

- 768 total square feet of living area
- Living room has an attractive box window for enjoying views
- The compact, yet efficient kitchen is open to the living room
- Six closets provide great storage for a compact plan
- Plans include optional third bedroom with an additional 288 square feet of living area
- 2 bedrooms, 1 bath
- Basement foundation, drawings also include crawl space and slab foundations

Opt Bed Plan 44'-0"
Std Floor Plan 32'-0"

24'-0"

Br 1
10-1x12-0

Kitchen
12-0x8-1

Storage

Br 2
13-5x8-8

Living Rm
15-2x14-11

Opt Bed
11-8x14-7

© Copyright by designer/architect

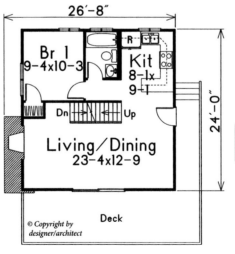

Ski Chalet With Style

- 1,680 total square feet of living area
- Highly functional lower level includes a wet hall with storage, laundry area, workshop and cozy ski lounge with an enormous fireplace
- First floor is warmed by a large fireplace in the living/dining area that features a spacious wrap-around deck
- Lots of sleeping space for guests or a large family
- 5 bedrooms, 2 1/2 baths
- Walk-out basement foundation

First Floor
576 sq. ft.

© Copyright by designer/architect

Second Floor
528 sq. ft.

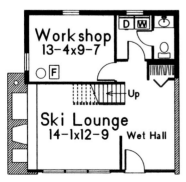

Lower Level
576 sq. ft.

Sensational Cottage Retreat

- 647 total square feet of living area
- Large vaulted room for living/sleeping has plant shelves on each end, a stone fireplace and wide glass doors to the deck
- Roomy kitchen is vaulted and has a bayed dining area and fireplace
- Step down into a sunken and vaulted bath featuring a 6'-0" whirlpool tub-in-a-bay with shelves at each end for storage
- A large palladian window adorns each end of the cottage giving a cheery atmosphere throughout
- 1 living/sleeping room, 1 bath
- Crawl space foundation

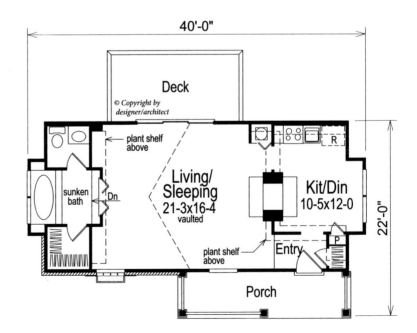

LOWE'S
LEGACY
SERIES

Compact Home Maximizes Space

- 987 total square feet of living area
- Galley kitchen opens into the cozy breakfast room
- Convenient coat closets are located by both entrances
- Dining/living room offers an expansive open area
- Breakfast room has access to the outdoors
- Front porch is great for enjoying outdoor living
- 3 bedrooms, 1 bath
- Basement foundation

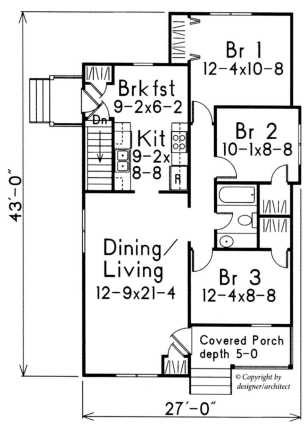

43'-0"

27'-0"

Br 1
12-4x10-8

Brkfst
9-2x6-2

Dn

Kit
9-2x
8-8

R

Br 2
10-1x8-8

Dining/
Living
12-9x21-4

Br 3
12-4x8-8

Covered Porch
depth 5-0

© Copyright by
designer/architect

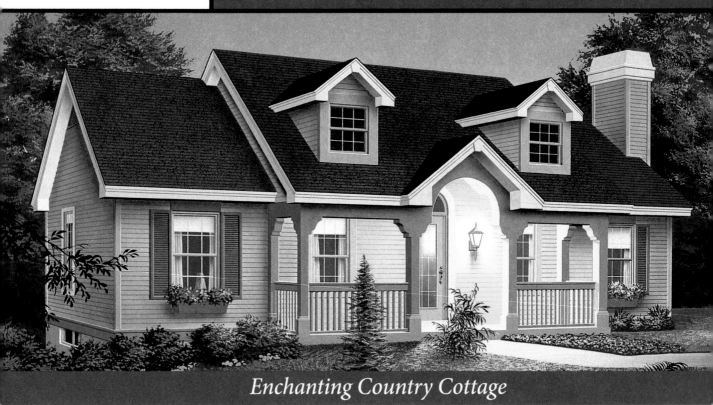

Enchanting Country Cottage

- 1,140 total square feet of living area
- Open and spacious living and dining areas for family gatherings
- Well-organized kitchen has an abundance of cabinetry and a built-in pantry
- Roomy master bath features a double-bowl vanity
- Plan also available with energy efficient R-Control® SIPs (Structural Insulated Panels), please call 1-877-379-3420 for more information
- 3 bedrooms, 2 baths, 2-car drive under rear entry garage
- Basement foundation

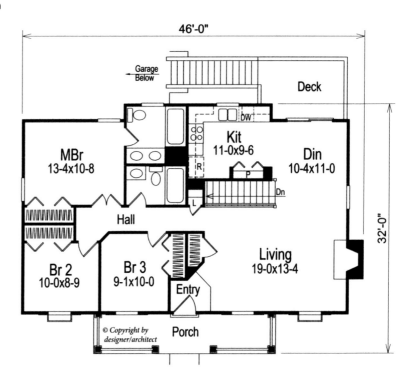

Handsome Home For A Narrow Lot

- 1,298 total square feet of living area
- The large great room features a dining area, corner fireplace and sliding doors to a rear veranda
- Open to the great room is a smartly-designed kitchen with snack counter built-in pantry and convenient adjacent laundry room with coat closet
- The brightly-lit breakfast area enjoys lots of windows including a bay with views of the veranda and beyond
- A luxury bath with a separate shower and garden tub, walk-in closet, double entry doors and a patio door with access to the veranda are the many amenities of the master bedroom
- 3 bedrooms, 2 baths, 2-car garage
- Slab foundation

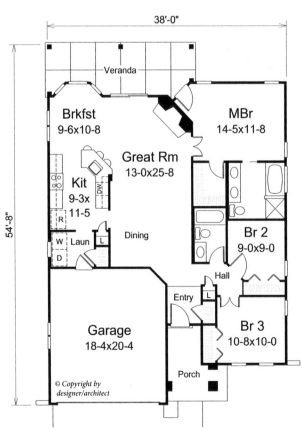

Cozy Vacation Home

- 809 total square feet of living area

- This attractive earth berm home is perfectly designed for a vacation retreat

- Nestled in a hillside with only one exposed exterior wall, this home offers efficiency, protection and affordability

- A large porch creates an ideal space for lazy afternoons and quiet evenings

- All rooms are very spacious and three closets plus the laundry room provide abundant storage

- 1 bedroom, 1 bath

- Slab foundation

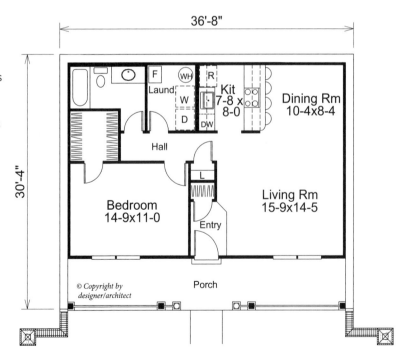

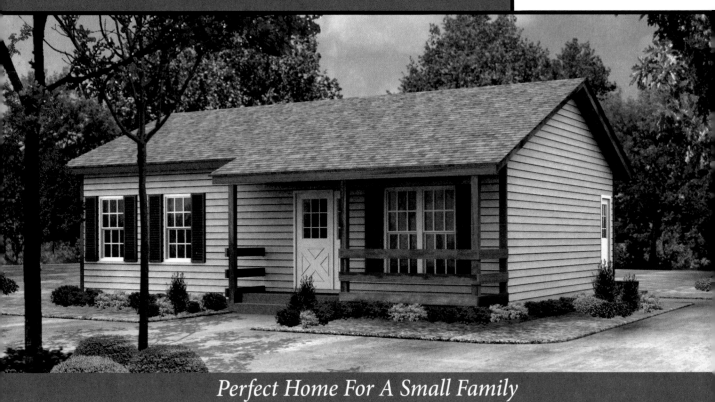

Perfect Home For A Small Family

- 864 total square feet of living area
- An L-shaped kitchen with convenient pantry is adjacent to the dining area
- This home has easy access to the laundry area, linen closet and storage closet
- Both bedrooms include ample closet space
- 2 bedrooms, 1 bath
- Crawl space foundation, drawings also include basement and slab foundations

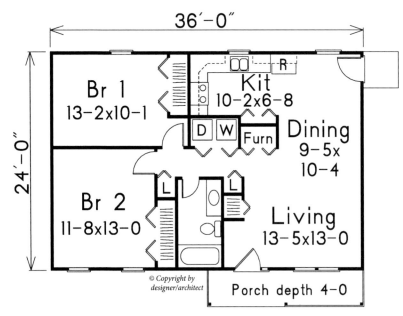

36′-0″

24′-0″

Br 1
13-2x10-1

Kit
10-2x6-8

D W Furn

Dining
9-5x
10-4

Br 2
11-8x13-0

Living
13-5x13-0

© Copyright by
designer/architect

Porch depth 4-0

Superb Floor Plan

- 1,999 total square feet of living area

- Delightful dormers and an inviting porch greet guests and add superb curb appeal

- Inside, the 17' vaulted living room ceiling increases spaciousness and a handy media center adds great organization

- An elegant three-sided fireplace adjoins both the living and dining rooms, adding grand style

- 3 bedrooms, 2 1/2 baths, 2-car side entry garage

- Basement foundation

Second Floor
672 sq. ft.

First Floor
1,327 sq. ft.

LOWE'S
LEGACY
SERIES

Cheerful Country Home

- 400 total square feet of living area
- This lovely cottage is ideal for a vacation home
- The large screened porch allows you to enjoy the outdoors in any weather
- A raised bar overlooks the living room and makes a nice transition from the kitchen
- 1 bedroom, 1 bath
- Slab foundation

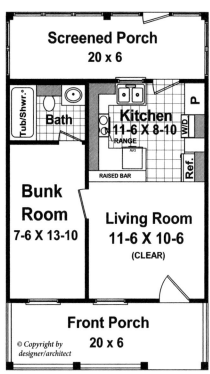

Screened Porch
20 x 6

Tub/Shwr.

Bath

Kitchen
11-6 X 8-10

RANGE

P

W/D

Ref.

RAISED BAR

Bunk Room
7-6 X 13-10

Living Room
11-6 X 10-6
(CLEAR)

© Copyright by designer/architect

Front Porch
20 x 6

Width: 22'-0"
Depth: 32'-0"

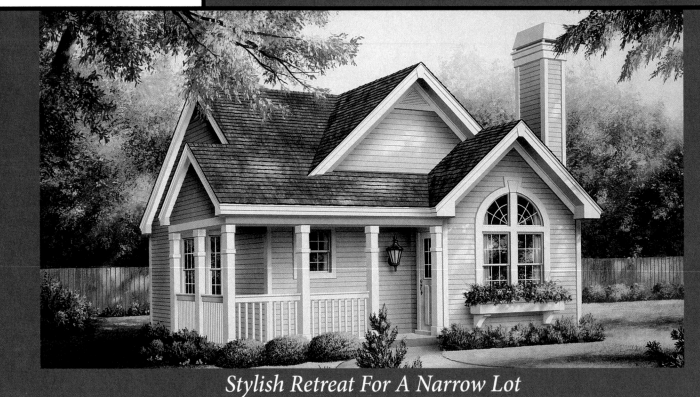

Stylish Retreat For A Narrow Lot

- 1,084 total square feet of living area
- Delightful country porch for quiet evenings
- The living room offers a front feature window which invites the sun and includes a fireplace and dining area with private patio
- The U-shaped kitchen features lots of cabinets and a bayed breakfast room with built-in pantry
- Both bedrooms have walk-in closets and access to their own bath
- 2 bedrooms, 2 baths
- Basement foundation

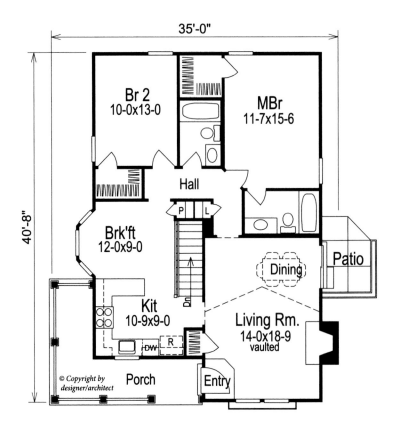

Comfortable And Cozy Cottage

- 421 total square feet of living area
- A recessed porch for protection from inclement weather adds charm to the exterior
- The living room features a large bay window, convenient kitchenette and an entry area with guest closet
- A full size bath and closet are provided for the bedroom
- 1 bedroom, 1 bath, 1-car garage
- Slab foundation

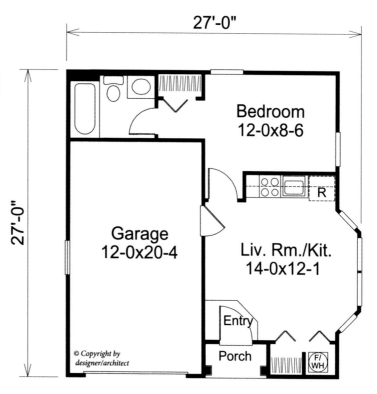

27'-0"

27'-0"

Bedroom
12-0x8-6

Garage
12-0x20-4

Liv. Rm./Kit.
14-0x12-1

R

Entry

Porch

F/WH

© Copyright by designer/architect

Casual Farmhouse Appeal

- 2,239 total square feet of living area

- Two sets of French doors in the family room lead to a covered porch ideal for relaxing

- The master bedroom has a spacious bath with an oversized tub placed in a sunny bay window

- Both second floor bedrooms have storage closets for terrific organizing

- 3 bedrooms, 2 1/2 baths, 2-car detached garage

- Basement foundation, drawings also include crawl space foundation

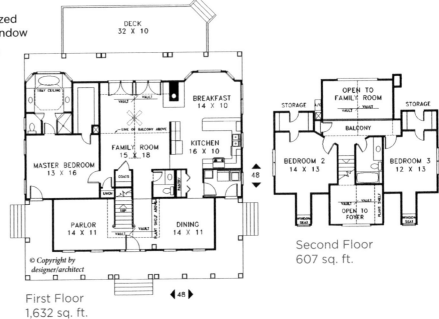

Plenty Of Room For The Growing Family

- 1,705 total square feet of living area
- Two bedrooms on the first floor for convenience and two bedrooms on the second for privacy
- L-shaped kitchen adjacent to dining room accesses the outdoors
- 2" x 6" exterior walls available, please order plan #539-001D-0110
- 4 bedrooms, 2 baths
- Crawl space foundation, drawings also include basement and slab foundations

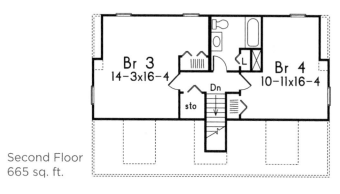

Second Floor
665 sq. ft.

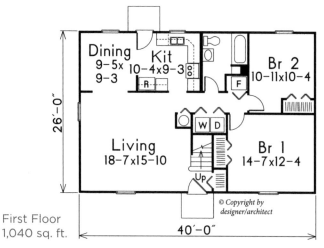

First Floor
1,040 sq. ft.

Enchanting Cottage Offers Exciting Getaway

- 1,075 total square feet of living area

- This charming exterior is achieved with extra steep gables, decorative trim, Old English window grilles, a second floor balcony with round-top door, flower boxes, swooping walls, and stucco columns with lanterns

- A very spacious entry with coat closet leads you down a few steps to the sunken living areas with wood-burning fireplace and a door to the rear covered patio

- The dining area with bay window is open to the living room and adjoining kitchen

- An ascending staircase takes you to the second floor bedroom with two closets, built-in shelves, plant shelf and a door to the front exterior balcony

- 1 bedroom, 1 bath, 1-car garage

- Crawl space foundation

First Floor
718 sq. ft.

Second Floor
357 sq. ft.

A Perfect Relaxed Ranch Home

- 1,227 total square feet of living area
- A coffered ceiling tops the master bedroom adding style and elegance to the interior
- The dining area flows effortlessly into the coffered family room with fireplace
- The U-shaped kitchen is compact, yet keeps everything within reach
- 3 bedrooms, 2 baths
- Slab foundation

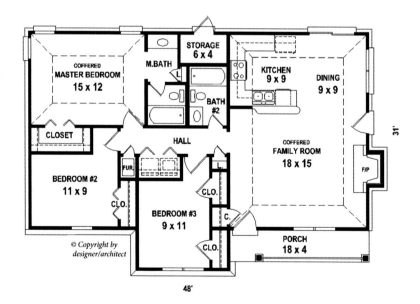

Simple, Affordable Lake Home

- 1,142 total square feet of living area

- The side garage allows for a more attractive exterior

- Open and airy, this plan includes a living room with bayed dining area, sliding glass doors to a large rear deck, coat closet and convenient powder room

- The U-shaped kitchen has a separate laundry space and pass-through breakfast bar

- The lower level consists of a hall bath, handy linen closet and two bedrooms that feature walk-in closets and sliding glass doors to the rear patio

- 2 bedrooms, 1 1/2 baths, 1-car garage

- Walk-out basement foundation

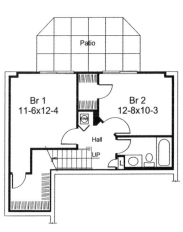

Lower Level
570 sq. ft.

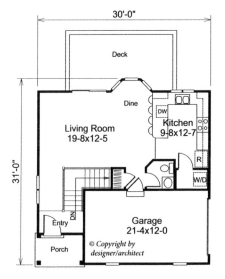

First Floor
572 sq. ft.

Convenient Ranch

- 1,120 total square feet of living area

- Master bedroom includes a half bath with laundry area, linen closet and kitchen access

- Kitchen has charming double-door entry, breakfast bar and a convenient walk-in pantry

- Welcoming front porch opens to a large living room with coat closet

- 3 bedrooms, 1 1/2 baths

- Crawl space foundation, drawings also include basement and slab foundations

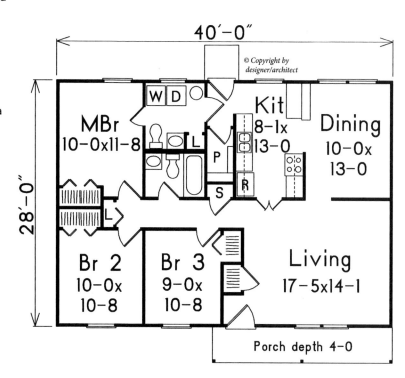

Luxurious Master Suite

- 2,058 total square feet of living area

- Designed for today's more narrow lots, this home adds style to any neighborhood

- All bedrooms are located on the second floor but are easily accessible thanks to a centrally located elevator

- The dramatic and spacious kitchen flows neatly from an angled pantry to the recipe desk and serving bar

- 3 bedrooms, 2 1/2 baths, 2-car garage

- Crawl space foundation

© Copyright by designer/architect

DECK
26'-5" x 9'-8"

BREAKFAST
8'-10" x 12'-10"

FAMILY
17'-2" x 14'-1"

KITCHEN
13'-2 x 18'-6"

ELEVATOR
7'-4" x 4'-4"

PANTRY

COATS

DINING
11'-0" x 14'-11"

DOOR TO BASEMENT

GARAGE
18'-0" x 24'-10"

43'-6"

PORCH
16'-0" x 5'-8"

35'-0"

First Floor
1,135 sq. ft.

BEDROOM 3
12'-4" x 11'-4"

HERS

VAULT

VAULT

ELEVATOR

LINEN

BEDROOM 2
11'-0" x 15'-6"

LAUNDRY
8'-1" x 5'-0"

MASTER SUITE
14'-6" x 15'-4"

TRAY CEILING

HIS

SITTING
7'-0" x 9'-2"

BALCONY

Second Floor
923 sq. ft.

To Order See Page 254 or Call Toll-Free 1-877-379-3420

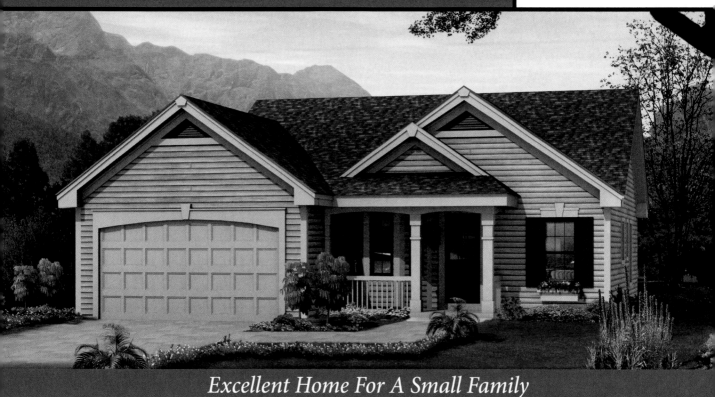

Excellent Home For A Small Family

- 1,062 total square feet of living area
- Handsome appeal is created by triple-gable facade
- An efficient U-shaped kitchen features a snack bar and breakfast room and is open to the living room with bay window
- Both the master bedroom, with its own private bath, and bedroom #2/study enjoy access to the rear patio
- 3 bedrooms, 2 baths, 2-car garage
- Basement foundation

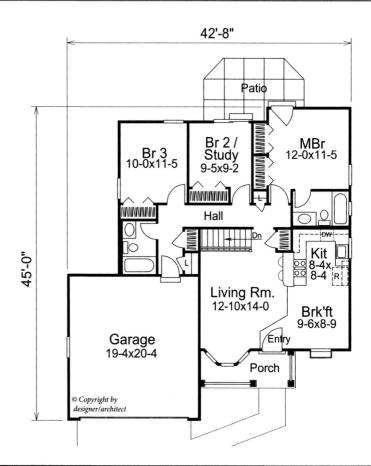

42'-8"

45'-0"

Patio

Br 3
10-0x11-5

Br 2 /
Study
9-5x9-2

MBr
12-0x11-5

Hall

Dn

DW

Kit
8-4x
8-4

R

Living Rm.
12-10x14-0

Brk'ft
9-6x8-9

Garage
19-4x20-4

Entry

Porch

© Copyright by
designer/architect

Compact And Stylish Design

- 1,100 total square feet of living area

- Designed with insulated concrete formed exterior walls providing a tighter construction, conserving heating and cooling energy consumption

- The two bedrooms are larger than you would expect for a house of this size, and one includes a private bath with a whirlpool tub

- A separate laundry room, pantry, linen and hall closet add convenient storage and workspace to this design

- Relax with friends and family on either the front or rear covered porches

- 2 bedrooms, 2 baths

- Slab foundation

Width: 31'-2"
Depth: 48'-6"

Rear Porch
12-8 x 9-0
© Copyright by designer/architect

Tub/Shwr.

Bath

Bedroom 1
11-6 x 13-0
9'-0" Clg. Ht.

Breakfast
12-0 x 7-2
9'-0" Clg. Ht.

Raised Bar

DW

Laundry

D

W

Kitchen
12-0 x 10-4

P

R

Raised Bar

C   C

Tub/Shwr.

Bath

Hall

C   L

Living Room
17-6 x 12-10
(CLEAR)
9'-0" Clg. Ht.

Bedroom 2
11-6 x 13-0
9'-0" Clg. Ht.

Front Porch
17-10 x 5-0

Split Bedroom Cottage Home

- 1,202 total square feet of living area

- All the necessary ingredients provided in a simple structure that's affordable to build

- The vaulted living room features a fireplace, dining area and access to the rear patio

- An angled snack bar is the highlight of this well-planned U-shaped kitchen

- 3 bedrooms, 2 baths, 2-car side entry garage

- Basement foundation, drawings also include slab and crawl space foundations

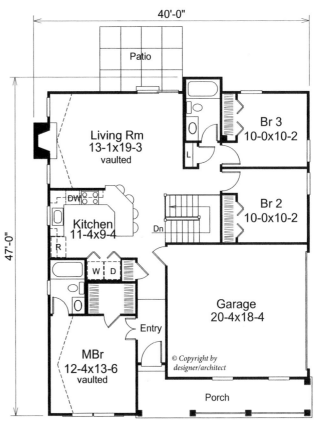

A Cottage With Class

- 576 total square feet of living area
- Perfect country retreat features vaulted living room and entry with skylights and a plant shelf above
- A double-door entry leads to the vaulted bedroom with bath access
- Kitchen offers generous storage and a pass-through breakfast bar
- 1 bedroom, 1 bath
- Crawl space foundation

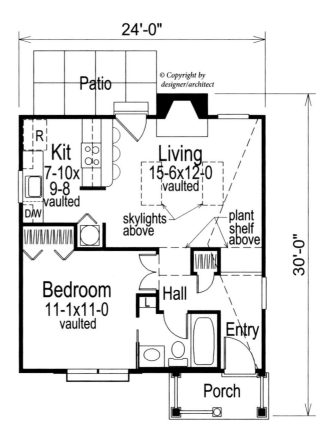

24'-0"

Patio

© Copyright by designer/architect

R

Kit
7-10x
9-8
vaulted

DW

Living
15-6x12-0
vaulted

skylights above

plant shelf above

Bedroom
11-1x11-0
vaulted

Hall

Entry

30'-0"

Porch

Charming Country Haven

- 1,525 total square feet of living area
- This appealing home features plenty of amenities and fits beautifully on a narrow lot
- The warm kitchen with a sunny breakfast nook is well designed to serve as the busiest room in the home
- Three bedrooms are located on the second floor for extra peace and quiet
- 3 bedrooms, 2 1/2 baths, 2-car garage
- Basement foundation, drawings also include slab foundation

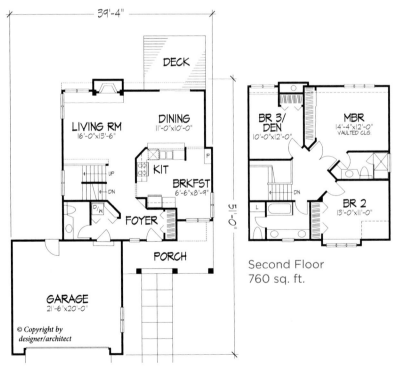

First Floor
765 sq. ft.

Second Floor
760 sq. ft.

Year-Round Hideaway

- 416 total square feet of living area
- Open floor plan creates a spacious feeling
- Covered porch has rustic appeal
- The kitchen offers plenty of cabinets and workspace
- Large linen closet is centrally located and close to the bath
- 2" x 6" exterior walls available, please order plan #539-058D-0076
- Sleeping area, 1 bath
- Slab foundation

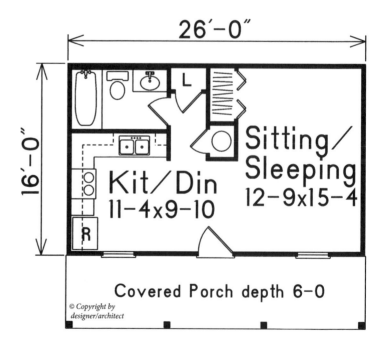

26'-0"

16'-0"

L

Kit/Din
11-4x9-10

R

Sitting/
Sleeping
12-9x15-4

Covered Porch depth 6-0

© Copyright by
designer/architect

Porches Enhance Small Retirement Or Starter Home

- 1,316 total square feet of living area
- Porches are accessible from entry, dining room and study/bedroom #2
- The living room enjoys a vaulted ceiling, corner fireplace and twin windows with an arched transom above
- A kitchen is provided with corner windows, an outdoor plant shelf, a snack bar, a built-in pantry and opens to a large dining room
- Bedrooms are very roomy, feature walk-in closets and have easy access to oversized baths
- 2 bedrooms, 2 baths, 2-car side entry garage
- Basement foundation, drawings also include crawl space and slab foundations

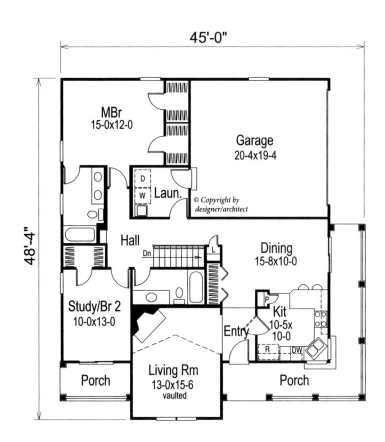

45'-0"

48'-4"

MBr
15-0x12-0

Garage
20-4x19-4

Laun.

© Copyright by
designer/architect

Hall

Dn

Dining
15-8x10-0

Study/Br 2
10-0x13-0

Entry

Kit
10-5x
10-0

Porch

Living Rm
13-0x15-6
vaulted

Porch

Double Dormers Accent This Cozy Vacation Retreat

- 581 total square feet of living area
- Kitchen/living room features space for dining and spiral steps leading to the loft area
- Large loft area can easily be converted to a bedroom or home office
- Entry space has a unique built-in display niche
- 1 bedroom, 1 bath
- Slab foundation

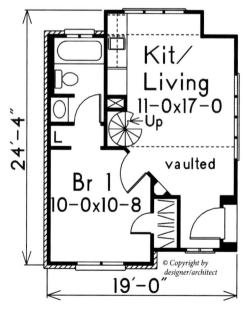

Kit/Living
11-0x17-0
Up
vaulted

Br 1
10-0x10-8

24'-4"

19'-0"

First Floor
449 sq. ft.

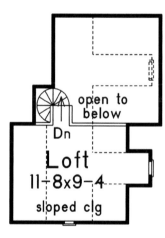

open to below
Dn

Loft
11-8x9-4
sloped clg

© Copyright by designer/architect

Second Floor
132 sq. ft.

Home For Narrow Lot Offers Wide Open Spaces

- 1,492 total square feet of living area
- Cleverly angled entry spills into the living and dining rooms that share warmth from the fireplace flanked by arched windows
- Master bedroom has a huge walk-in closet, and private bath with shower
- Stucco and dutch-hipped roofs add warmth and charm to the facade
- 3 bedrooms, 2 1/2 baths, 2-car garage
- Basement foundation

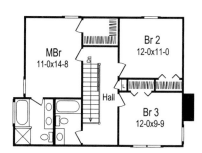

Second Floor
732 sq. ft.

First Floor
760 sq. ft.

Covered Porch Highlights This Home

- 1,364 total square feet of living area

- Bedrooms are separated from the living areas for privacy

- Master bedroom has a private bath and large walk-in closet

- Laundry area is conveniently located near the kitchen

- Bright and spacious living room

- U-shaped kitchen is designed to keep everything within reach

- 3 bedrooms, 2 baths, optional 2-car garage

- Basement foundation

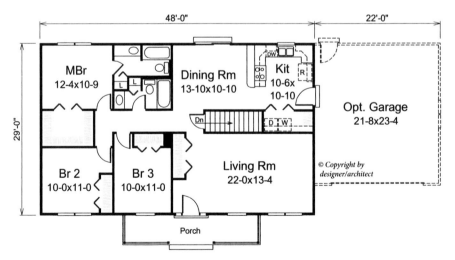

Wonderful Entertaining Possibilities

- 1,200 total square feet of living area

- Large living and dining rooms are completely open to one another with lots of space for large family gatherings

- The cozy kitchen has a half-wall open to the dining room offering lots of entertaining possibilities

- All three bedrooms have nice-sized closets and share a hall bath

- An optional second bath is available at rear of home

- 3 bedrooms, 1 bath, optional 2-car garage

- Basement foundation, drawings also include crawl space and slab foundations

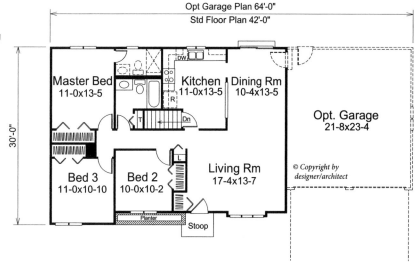

Opt Garage Plan 64'-0"
Std Floor Plan 42'-0"
30'-0"

Master Bed
11-0x13-5

Kitchen
11-0x13-5

Dining Rm
10-4x13-5

Opt. Garage
21-8x23-4

Bed 3
11-0x10-10

Bed 2
10-0x10-2

Living Rm
17-4x13-7

© Copyright by designer/architect

Planter

Stoop

Decorative Window Enhances Facade

- 1,539 total square feet of living area
- This two-story home is ideal for a narrow lot
- The front half of the first floor consists of the combined family room, kitchen and dining area while the rear houses the master bedroom, utility and half bath
- Two secondary bedrooms and a bath on the second floor round out this efficient design
- 3 bedrooms, 2 1/2 baths, 2-car rear entry garage
- Slab foundation, drawings also include basement foundation

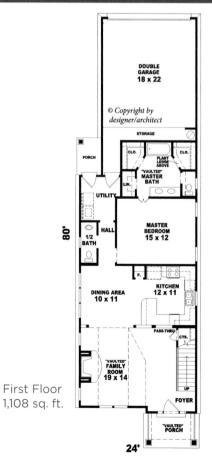

Second Floor
431 sq. ft.

First Floor
1,108 sq. ft.

Delightful Victorian

- 1,985 total square feet of living area
- Cozy family room features a fireplace and double French doors opening onto the porch
- The open kitchen includes a convenient island
- The extraordinary master bedroom has a tray ceiling and a large walk-in closet
- Lovely bayed breakfast area has easy access to the deck
- 3 bedrooms, 2 1/2 baths
- Partial basement/crawl space foundation

© Copyright by designer/architect

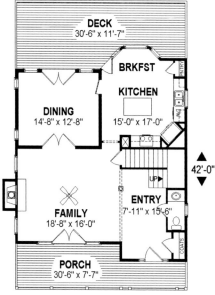

DECK
30'-6" x 11'-7"

BRKFST

KITCHEN
15'-0" x 17'-0"

DINING
14'-8" x 12'-8"

42'-0"

UP

FAMILY
18'-8" x 16'-0"

ENTRY
7'-11" x 15'-6"

COATS

PORCH
30'-6" x 7'-7"

First Floor ◀ 31'-2" ▶
1,009 sq. ft.

TRAY CEILING

MASTER BDRM
16'-4" x 15'-0"

D W

DN

BEDROOM 2
12'-0" x 12'-8"

BEDROOM 3
12'-8" x 12'-0"

WINDOW SEAT

Second Floor
976 sq. ft.

Cozy Front Porch Welcomes Guests

- 1,393 total square feet of living area
- L-shaped kitchen features a walk-in pantry, island cooktop and is convenient to the laundry room and dining area
- Master bedroom features a large walk-in closet and private bath with separate tub and shower
- Convenient storage/coat closet in hall
- View to the patio from the dining area
- 3 bedrooms, 2 baths, 2-car detached garage
- Crawl space foundation, drawings also include slab foundation

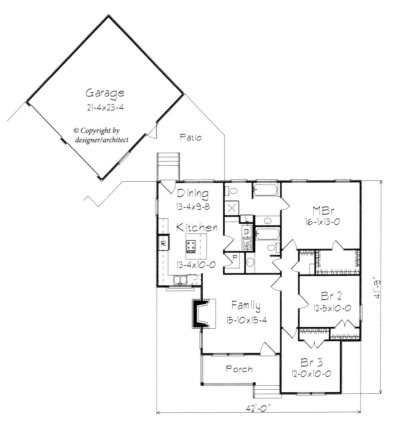

Ideal Design For A Narrow Lot

- 983 total square feet of living area
- Spacious front porch leads you into the living and dining areas open to a pass-through kitchen
- A small patio with privacy fence creates exterior access from the living room
- The master bedroom includes a large walk-in closet and its own private full bath
- 3 bedrooms, 2 baths, 2-car garage
- Crawl space foundation, drawings also include slab foundation

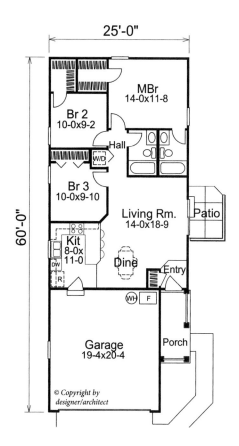

Large Bay Graces Dining Area And Master Bedroom

- 1,818 total square feet of living area
- Spacious living and dining rooms
- Master bedroom has a walk-in closet, dressing area and bath
- Convenient carport and storage area
- 2" x 6" exterior walls available, please order plan #539-001D-0113
- 3 bedrooms, 2 1/2 baths, 1-car carport
- Crawl space foundation, drawings also include basement and slab foundations

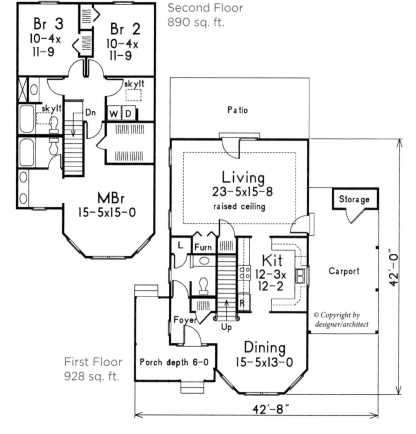

Second Floor
890 sq. ft.

Br 3
10-4x
11-9

Br 2
10-4x
11-9

skylt

skylt Dn W D

MBr
15-5x15-0

Patio

Living
23-5x15-8
raised ceiling

Storage

L Furn

Kit
12-3x
12-2

Carport

42'-0"

© Copyright by
designer/architect

Foyer Up

First Floor
928 sq. ft.

Porch depth 6-0

Dining
15-5x13-0

42'-8"

Functional Design For Compact Lot

- 1,153 total square feet of living area

- The arched window, detailed brickwork and roof dormer all combine to create a stylish and inviting exterior

- A fireplace, U-shaped kitchen with built-in pantry and dining area with view to a side fenced patio are the many features of the living room area

- The master bedroom includes a private bath, walk-in closet and access to the patio area

- 3 bedrooms, 2 baths, 2-car garage

- Basement foundation

37'-4"

47'-8"

Br 2
11-0x11-0

MBr
12-3x13-0

Br 3
11-0x9-0

Hall

Kitchen
12-3x9-2

R

P

DW

DN

L

Dine

Patio

Living Room
14-8x17-10

Garage
19-4x20-4

Entry

Porch

© Copyright by designer/architect

Country Cottage Offers A Large Vaulted Living Space

- 962 total square feet of living area
- Both the kitchen and family room share warmth from the fireplace
- Charming facade features a covered porch on one side, screened porch on the other and attractive planter boxes
- L-shaped kitchen boasts a convenient pantry
- 2 bedrooms, 1 bath
- Crawl space foundation

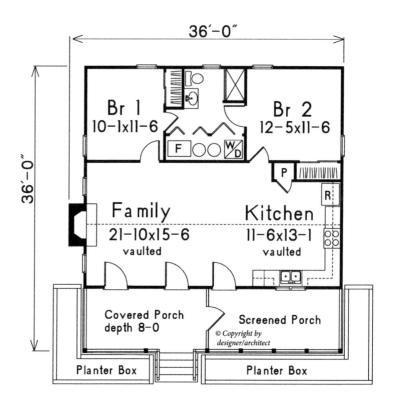

36'-0"

36'-0"

Br 1
10-1x11-6

Br 2
12-5x11-6

F   W D   P   R

Family
21-10x15-6
vaulted

Kitchen
11-6x13-1
vaulted

Covered Porch
depth 8-0

Screened Porch

© Copyright by
designer/architect

Planter Box

Planter Box

Cozy Retreat For Weekends

- 480 total square feet of living area

- Inviting wrap-around porch and rear covered patio are perfect for summer evenings

- Living room features a fireplace, separate entry foyer with coat closet and sliding doors to a rear patio

- The compact, but complete kitchen includes a dining area with bay window and window at sink for patio views

- 1 bedroom, 1 bath, 1-car garage

- Slab foundation

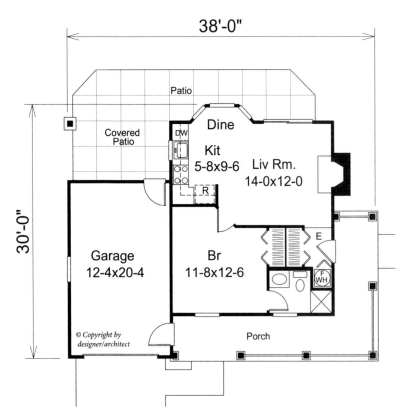

Country Appeal For A Small Lot

- 1,299 total square feet of living area
- Large front porch for enjoying relaxing evenings
- First floor master bedroom has a bay window, walk-in closet and roomy bath
- Two generous bedrooms with lots of closet space, a hall bath, linen closet and balcony overlook comprise the second floor
- 3 bedrooms, 2 1/2 baths
- Basement foundation

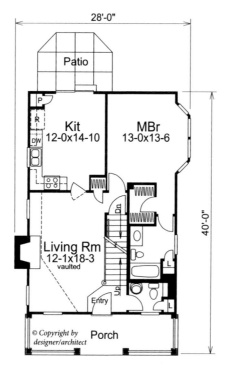

First Floor
834 sq. ft.

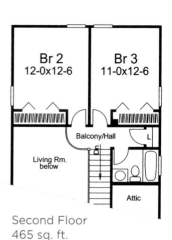

Second Floor
465 sq. ft.

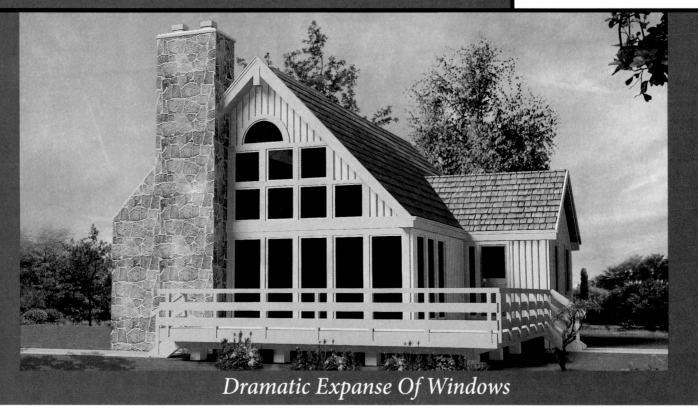

Dramatic Expanse Of Windows

- 1,660 total square feet of living area
- Energy efficient home with 2" x 6" exterior walls
- Convenient gear and equipment room
- Spacious living and dining rooms look even larger with the openness of the foyer and kitchen
- Large wrap-around deck is a great plus for outdoor living
- Broad balcony overlooks the living and dining rooms
- 3 bedrooms, 3 baths
- Partial basement/crawl space foundation, drawings also include slab foundation

Br 2
11-0x12-0

MBr
12-0x12-0

Br 3
14-10x12-0

Equip.

skylt

Up

Kitchen
12-7x7-6

Balcony

open to below

Living
12-9x15-7
vaulted

Dining
12-9x14-0
vaulted

Second Floor
368 sq. ft.

© Copyright by
designer/architect

Deck

First Floor
1,292 sq. ft.

41'-5"

44'-1"

Smaller Home Offers Stylish Exterior

- 1,700 total square feet of living area

- Two-story entry with T-shaped stairs is illuminated with a decorative oval window

- Skillfully designed U-shaped kitchen has a built-in pantry

- All bedrooms have generous closet storage and are common to a spacious hall with a walk-in cedar closet

- 4 bedrooms, 2 1/2 baths, 2-car side entry garage

- Basement foundation

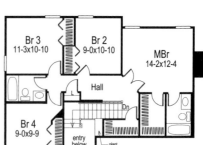

Second Floor
804 sq. ft.

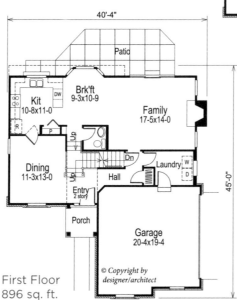

© Copyright by
designer/architect

First Floor
896 sq. ft.

Well-Designed Home Makes Great Use Of Space

- 1,948 total square feet of living area
- Family room offers warmth with an oversized fireplace and rustic beamed ceiling
- Fully-appointed kitchen extends into the family room
- Practical mud room is adjacent to the kitchen
- 3 bedrooms, 3 baths
- Basement foundation, drawings also include crawl space foundation

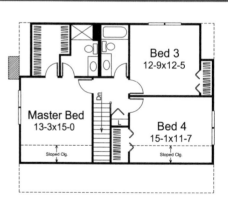

Second Floor
868 sq. ft.

First Floor
1,080 sq. ft.

French Country Style For A Narrow Lot

- 1,519 total square feet of living area
- The large living room boasts a vaulted ceiling with plant shelf, fireplace, and opens to the bayed dining area
- Two walk-in closets, a stylish bath and small sitting area accompany the master bedroom
- The kitchen has an adjoining laundry/mud room and features a vaulted ceiling, snack counter open to the living and dining areas and a built-in pantry
- 4 bedrooms, 2 baths, 2-car garage
- Crawl space foundation, drawings also include slab and basement foundations

LOWE'S
LEGACY
SERIES

Dormer And Covered Porch Add To Country Charm

- 954 total square feet of living area
- Kitchen has a cozy bayed eating area
- Master bedroom has a walk-in closet and private bath
- Large great room has access to the back porch
- Convenient coat closet is located near the front entry
- 3 bedrooms, 2 baths
- Basement foundation

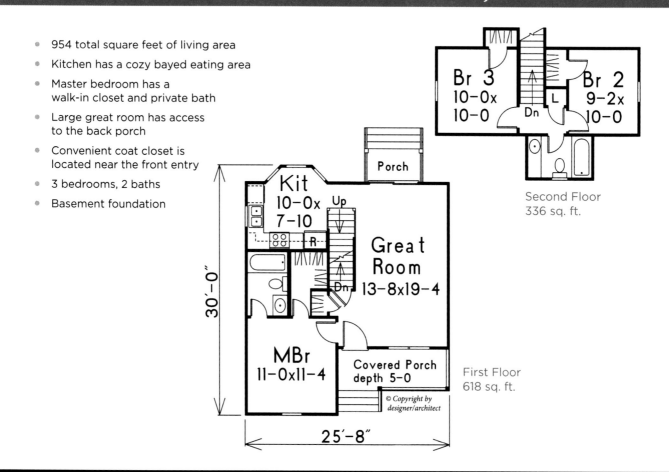

Br 3
10-0x
10-0

Br 2
9-2x
10-0

Dn

L

Second Floor
336 sq. ft.

Porch

Kit
10-0x
7-10

Up

R

Great
Room
13-8x19-4

Dn

30'-0"

MBr
11-0x11-4

Covered Porch
depth 5-0

© Copyright by
designer/architect

First Floor
618 sq. ft.

25'-8"

Perfect Home By The Sea

- 1,504 total square feet of living area
- The covered porch, unique square windows with custom grilles, decorative wall extensions and designer dormer all contribute to pleasing aesthetics for a paradise retreat
- Double-entry glass doors welcome you into an L-shaped entry foyer with handy guest closet
- The open and airy great room has a corner fireplace, dining area bay window and 9' glass sliding doors to rear patio
- A snack bar and adjacent laundry room are useful features of the spacious kitchen
- The master bedroom offers a large luxury bath, walk-in closet and a glass door to rear patio
- 2 bedrooms, 2 baths, 2-car side garage
- Slab foundation, drawings also include crawl space and basement foundations

LOWE'S
LEGACY
SERIES

Gabled Front Porch Adds Charm And Value

- 1,443 total square feet of living area

- A raised foyer and a cathedral ceiling in the living room add character to the interior

- Impressive tall-wall fireplace between the living and dining rooms

- Open U-shaped kitchen features a cheerful breakfast bay

- Angular side deck accentuates patio and garden

- First floor master bedroom has a walk-in closet and a corner window

- 3 bedrooms, 2 baths, 2-car garage

- Basement foundation

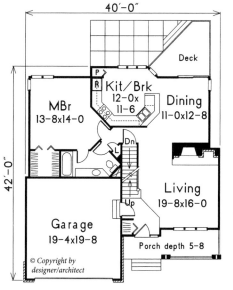

First Floor
1,006 sq. ft.

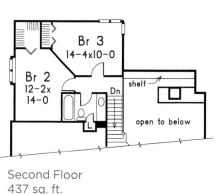

Second Floor
437 sq. ft.

Charming Covered Front Porch

- 2,547 total square feet of living area

- Second floor makes economical use of area above garage allowing for three bedrooms and a study/fourth bedroom

- First floor study is ideal for a home office

- Large pantry is located in the efficient kitchen

- 2" x 6" exterior walls available, please order plan #539-058D-0092

- 3 bedrooms, 2 1/2 baths, 2-car garage

- Basement foundation

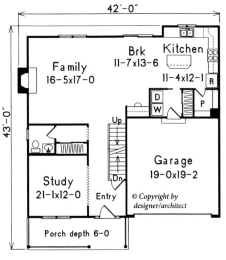

First Floor
1,083 sq. ft.

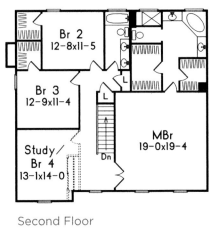

Second Floor
1,464 sq. ft.

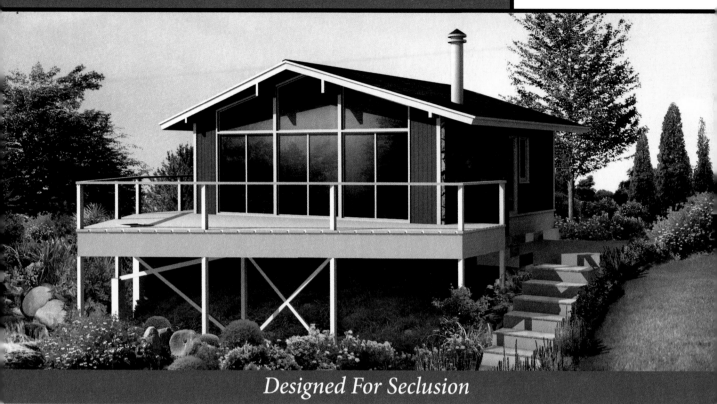

Designed For Seclusion

- 624 total square feet of living area

- The combination of stone, vertical siding, lots of glass and a low roof line creates a cozy retreat

- Vaulted living area features a free-standing fireplace that heats the adjacent stone wall

- Efficient kitchen includes a dining area and view onto an angular deck

- Two bedrooms share a hall bath with shower

- 2 bedrooms, 1 bath

- Pier foundation

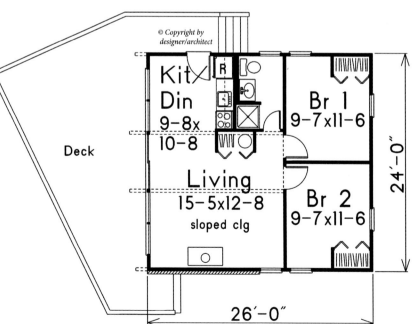

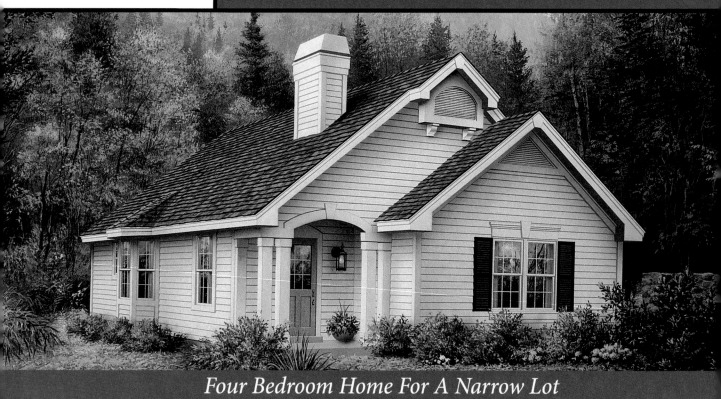

Four Bedroom Home For A Narrow Lot

- 1,452 total square feet of living area
- Large living room features a cozy corner fireplace, bayed dining area and access from the entry with guest closet
- Forward master bedroom enjoys having its own bath and linen closet
- Three additional bedrooms share a bath with a double-bowl vanity
- 2" x 6" exterior walls available, please order plan #539-007E-0102
- 4 bedrooms, 2 baths
- Basement foundation

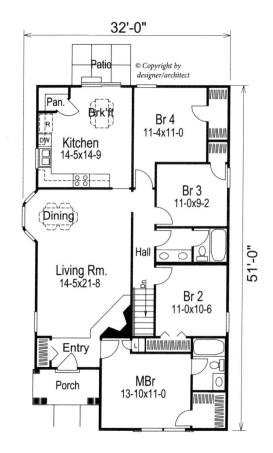

32'-0"

© Copyright by designer/architect

Patio

Pan.

Brk'ff

Kitchen
14-5x14-9

Br 4
11-4x11-0

Br 3
11-0x9-2

Dining

Hall

Living Rm.
14-5x21-8

Br 2
11-0x10-6

Entry

Porch

MBr
13-10x11-0

51'-0"

Attractive Dormers Enhance Facade

- 2,112 total square feet of living area
- Kitchen efficiently connects to the formal dining area
- A nook is located between the family room and kitchen creating an ideal breakfast area
- Both baths on the second floor feature skylights
- 3 bedrooms, 3 baths
- Basement foundation, drawings also include crawl space foundation

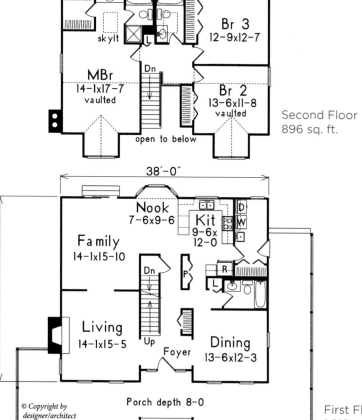

Second Floor
896 sq. ft.

First Floor
1,216 sq. ft.

© Copyright by designer/architect

Great Porch Opportunities

- 953 total square feet of living area
- Covered front and rear porches feature ceiling fans to keep you comfortable in warmer weather
- Two generous bedrooms, each with a walk-in closet, share a spacious bathroom
- A dramatic vaulted ceiling crowns the open family room and kitchen
- 2 bedrooms, 1 1/2 baths
- Crawl space foundation

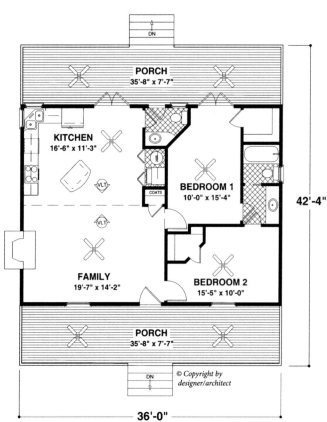

DN

PORCH
35'-8" x 7'-7"

KITCHEN
16'-6" x 11'-3"

VLT

COATS

VLT

BEDROOM 1
10'-0" x 15'-4"

42'-4"

FAMILY
19'-7" x 14'-2"

BEDROOM 2
15'-5" x 10'-0"

PORCH
35'-8" x 7'-7"

DN

© Copyright by designer/architect

36'-0"

Compact Home For Sloping Lot

- 1,332 total square feet of living area

- Home offers both basement and first floor entry locations

- A dramatic living room features a vaulted ceiling, fireplace, exterior balcony and dining area

- An L-shaped kitchen offers spacious cabinetry, breakfast area with bay window and access to the rear patio

- 2″ x 6″ exterior walls available, please order plan #539-007E-0087

- 3 bedrooms, 2 baths, 4-car tandem garage

- Walk-out basement foundation

© Copyright by designer/architect

First Floor
828 sq. ft.

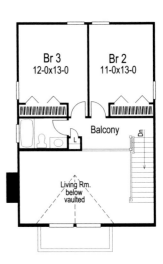

Second Floor
504 sq. ft.

Perfect Home For Escaping To The Outdoors

- 1,200 total square feet of living area

- Enjoy lazy summer evenings on this magnificent porch

- Activity area has a fireplace and ascending stair to the cozy loft

- Kitchen features a built-in pantry

- Master bedroom enjoys a large bath, walk-in closet and cozy loft overlooking the activity room below

- 2 bedrooms, 2 baths

- Crawl space foundation

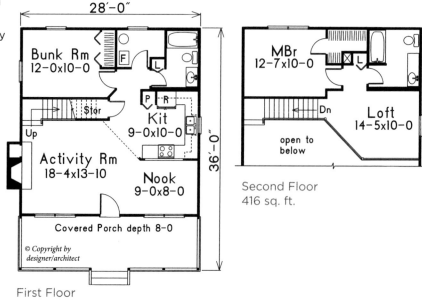

28'-0"

Bunk Rm
12-0x10-0

F

L

Up
Stor

Kit
9-0x10-0

P
R

Activity Rm
18-4x13-10

Nook
9-0x8-0

36'-0"

Covered Porch depth 8-0

© Copyright by
designer/architect

First Floor
784 sq. ft.

MBr
12-7x10-0

L

Dn

Loft
14-5x10-0

open to
below

Second Floor
416 sq. ft.

Charming Cottage

- 600 total square feet of living area
- This small home features a spacious living room that connects to the efficient kitchen with a raised snack bar
- The kitchen and bedroom access the rear porch and covered or screened porch that offers exceptional outdoor living space
- A bonus room is provided for a hobby room or second bedroom and is included in the square footage
- 1 bedroom, 1 bath
- Slab foundation, drawings also include basement and crawl space foundations

Width: 30'-0"
Depth: 32'-0"

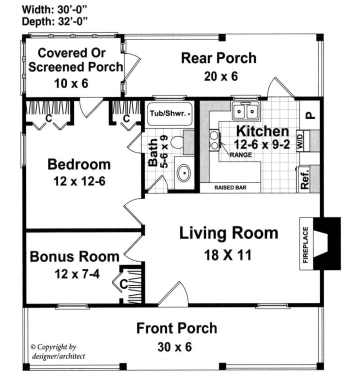

Covered Or Screened Porch
10 x 6

Rear Porch
20 x 6

Bath
5-6 x 9

Tub/Shwr.

Kitchen
12-6 x 9-2

RANGE

W/D

P

Ref.

Bedroom
12 x 12-6

RAISED BAR

Living Room
18 X 11

FIREPLACE

Bonus Room
12 x 7-4

C

© Copyright by designer/architect

Front Porch
30 x 6

Quaint Exterior, Full Front Porch

- 1,668 total square feet of living area
- The kitchen features a stylish pass-through to the living room
- Master bedroom is secluded from the living area for privacy
- Large windows in the kitchen/breakfast area creates a bright and cheerful atmosphere
- 3 bedrooms, 2 1/2 baths, 2-car side entry drive under garage
- Walk-out basement foundation

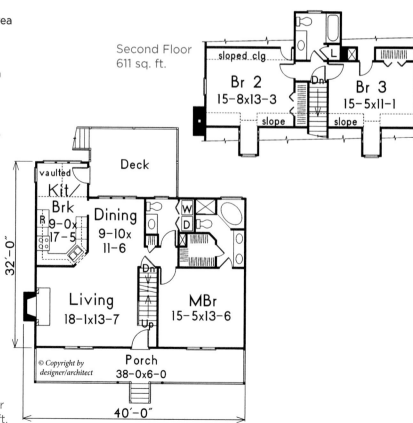

Second Floor
611 sq. ft.

sloped clg

Br 2
15-8x13-3

Br 3
15-5x11-1

slope   slope

Deck

vaulted

Kit/
Brk
9-0x
17-5

Dining
9-10x
11-6

W
D

Living
18-1x13-7

MBr
15-5x13-6

Dn

Up

© Copyright by designer/architect

Porch
38-0x6-0

First Floor
1,057 sq. ft.

32'-0"

40'-0"

Summer Retreat Or Year-Round Home

- 1,403 total square feet of living area
- Impressive living areas for a modest-sized home
- Special master/hall bath has linen storage, step-up tub and lots of window light
- Spacious closets everywhere you look
- 3 bedrooms, 2 baths, 2-car drive under garage
- Basement foundation

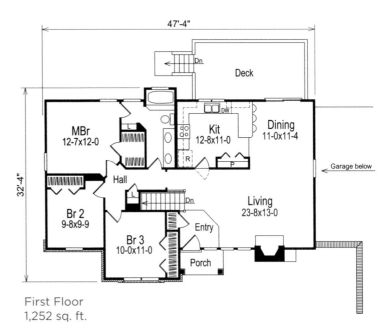

First Floor
1,252 sq. ft.

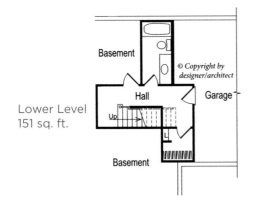

Lower Level
151 sq. ft.

Cheerful Farmhouse Design

- 1,456 total square feet of living area
- A beautiful fireplace is the focal point in the cozy family room
- The formal dining room, located between the kitchen and family room, is positioned perfectly for entertaining
- The bonus room above the garage has an additional 182 square feet of living area
- 3 bedrooms, 2 1/2 baths, 2-car garage
- Basement foundation

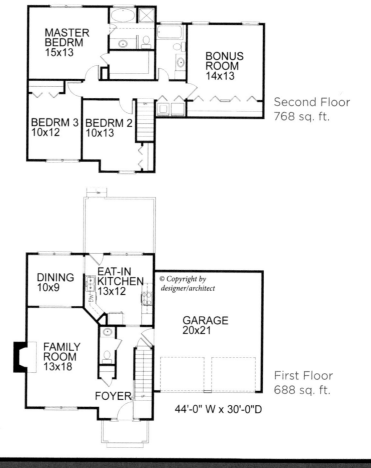

MASTER BEDRM 15x13

BONUS ROOM 14x13

BEDRM 3 10x12   BEDRM 2 10x13

Second Floor 768 sq. ft.

DINING 10x9   EAT-IN KITCHEN 13x12

© Copyright by designer/architect

GARAGE 20x21

FAMILY ROOM 13x18

FOYER

First Floor 688 sq. ft.

44'-0" W x 30'-0"D

Efficient Layout In This Multi-Level Home

- 1,617 total square feet of living area
- Kitchen and breakfast area overlook the great room with fireplace
- Formal dining room features a vaulted ceiling and an elegant circle-top window
- All bedrooms are located on the second floor for privacy
- 3 bedrooms, 2 1/2 baths, 2-car garage
- Partial crawl space/slab foundation

Second Floor
741 sq. ft.

First Floor
876 sq. ft.

Vacation Paradise

- 960 total square feet of living area
- Interesting roof and wood beams overhang a generous-sized deck
- Family room is vaulted and opens to the dining area and kitchen
- The kitchen has been skillfully designed for great efficiency
- Two bedrooms and a hall bath are located at the rear of home
- 2 bedrooms, 1 bath
- Crawl space foundation

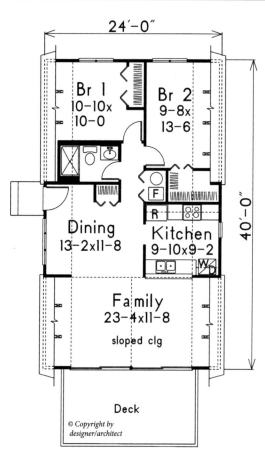

Compact Two-Story For A Small Site

- 1,167 total square feet of living area
- Attractive exterior is enhanced with multiple gables
- Sizable living room features a separate entry foyer and view to the front porch
- Functional kitchen has a breakfast room with bay window, built-in pantry and laundry room with half bath
- The master bedroom offers three closets and a luxury bath
- 2 bedrooms, 2 1/2 baths, 1-car garage
- Basement foundation

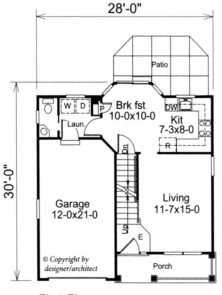

First Floor
476 sq. ft.

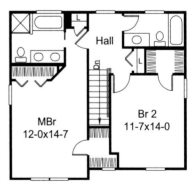

Second Floor
691 sq. ft.

The Answer To A Tapered Lot

- 986 total square feet of living area
- Wide and tall windows in the kitchen, dining and living rooms create bright and cheerful spaces
- Three bedrooms with plenty of closet space and an oversized hall bath are located at the rear of the home
- An extra-deep garage has storage space at the rear and access to the patio behind the garage
- Convenient linen closet is located in the hall
- 3 bedrooms, 1 bath, 1-car garage
- Basement foundation, drawings also include crawl space and slab foundations

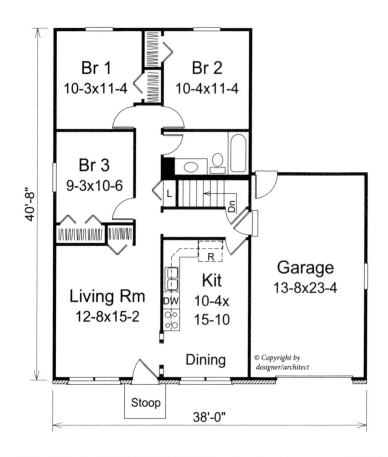

Style And Economics Meet

- 1,839 total square feet of living area

- Energy efficient home with 2" x 6" exterior walls

- An abundance of front-facing windows help to keep this berm home bright and cheerful

- The centrally located kitchen easily serves the more formal living and dining rooms as well as the casual family room

- The master bedroom enjoys private access to the bath

- 3 bedrooms, 1 bath

- Slab foundation

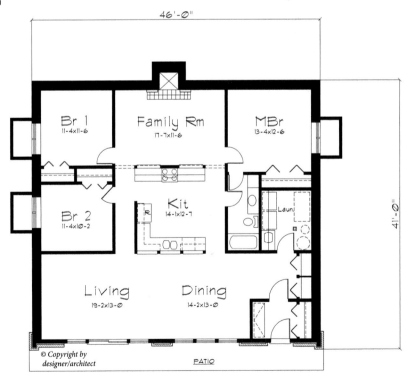

Stylish And Efficient Ranch

- 1,366 total square feet of living area
- Energy efficient home with 2" x 6" exterior walls
- A delightful front porch opens into the roomy living area, perfect for family gatherings
- The kitchen features a wrap-around counter connecting to the dining room that enjoys access to the backyard
- Relax in the master bedroom suite that offers a private bath, dressing area and walk-in closet
- 2 bedrooms, 2 baths, 2-car garage
- Basement foundation

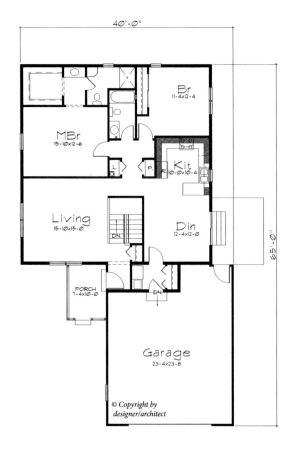

Large Great Room And Dining Area

- 1,160 total square feet of living area
- U-shaped kitchen includes a breakfast bar and convenient laundry area
- Master bedroom features a private half bath and large closet
- Dining room has outdoor access
- Dining and great rooms combine to create an open living atmosphere
- 3 bedrooms, 1 1/2 baths
- Crawl space foundation, drawings also include basement and slab foundations

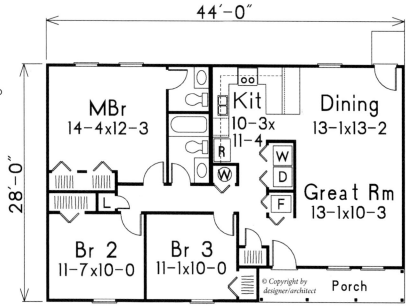

Comfortable Vacation Retreat

- 1,073 total square feet of living area
- Home includes a lovely covered front porch and a screened porch off the dining area
- Attractive box window brightens the kitchen
- Space for an efficiency washer and dryer is located conveniently between the bedrooms
- Family room is spotlighted by a fireplace with flanking bookshelves and spacious vaulted ceiling
- 2 bedrooms, 1 bath
- Crawl space foundation

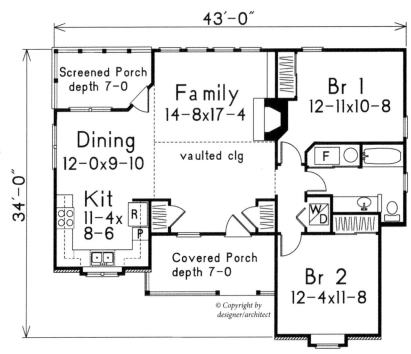

43'-0"

34'-0"

Screened Porch
depth 7-0

Family
14-8x17-4

Br 1
12-11x10-8

vaulted clg

Dining
12-0x9-10

Kit
11-4x
8-6

R
P

W
D

F

Covered Porch
depth 7-0

Br 2
12-4x11-8

© Copyright by
designer/architect

Special Planning In This Compact Home

- 977 total square feet of living area
- Comfortable living room features a vaulted ceiling, fireplace, plant shelf and coat closet
- Both bedrooms are located on the second floor and share a bath with a double-bowl vanity and linen closet
- Sliding glass doors in the dining room provide access to the deck
- 2 bedrooms, 1 1/2 baths, 1-car garage
- Basement foundation

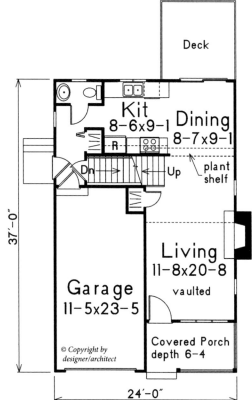

Deck

Kit
8-6x9-1

Dining
8-7x9-1

plant shelf

Dn   Up

Living
11-8x20-8
vaulted

Garage
11-5x23-5

© Copyright by designer/architect

Covered Porch
depth 6-4

37'-0"

24'-0"

First Floor
545 sq. ft.

Br 2
9-1x10-1

Dn

Br 1
11-5x11-2

Second Floor
432 sq. ft.

Rustic Design With Modern Features

- 1,000 total square feet of living area
- Large mud room has a separate covered porch entrance
- Full-length covered front porch
- Bedrooms are on opposite sides of the home for privacy
- The dining and family rooms combine for an open and spacious feeling
- 2" x 6" exterior walls available, please order plan #539-058D-0085
- 2 bedrooms, 1 bath
- Crawl space foundation

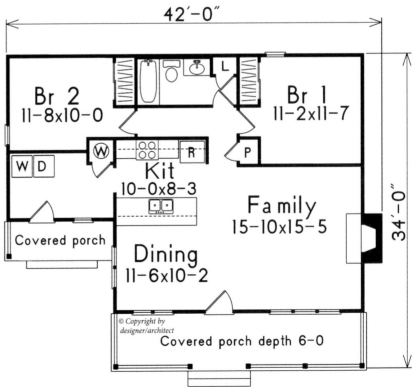

Ideal Two-Story For A Narrow Lot

- 1,674 total square feet of living area
- Energy efficient home with 2" x 6" exterior walls
- Covered entrance opens to find open living and dining rooms that are designed for entertaining
- A quiet study could also be used as a guest bedroom
- The master bedroom is secluded on the first floor while two additional bedrooms share the second floor
- 3 bedrooms, 2 baths
- Basement foundation

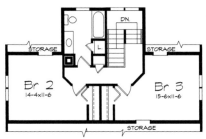

Second Floor
570 sq. ft.

First Floor
1,104 sq. ft.

© Copyright by designer/architect

Open Living Space Creates Comfortable Atmosphere

- 1,000 total square feet of living area

- Bath includes convenient closeted laundry area

- Master bedroom includes double closets and private access to the bath

- The foyer features a handy coat closet

- L-shaped kitchen provides easy access outdoors

- 3 bedrooms, 1 bath

- Crawl space foundation, drawings also include basement and slab foundations

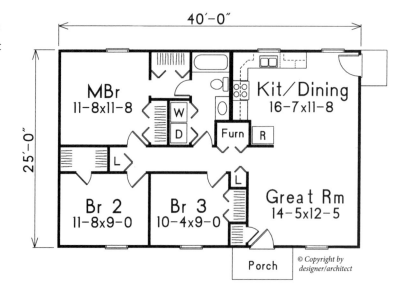

40'-0"

25'-0"

MBr
11-8x11-8

Kit/Dining
16-7x11-8

W
D

Furn R

L

Br 2
11-8x9-0

Br 3
10-4x9-0

L

Great Rm
14-5x12-5

Porch

© Copyright by designer/architect

Sensational Breakfast Area

- 1,610 total square feet of living area
- Attractive stone facade wraps around cozy breakfast room bay
- Roomy foyer leads to a splendid kitchen with an abundance of storage and counterspace
- The spacious living and dining room combination features access to the rear deck
- Master bedroom features a walk-in closet and compartmented bath with a luxurious garden tub
- 3 bedrooms, 2 baths
- Basement foundation, drawings also include crawl space and slab foundations

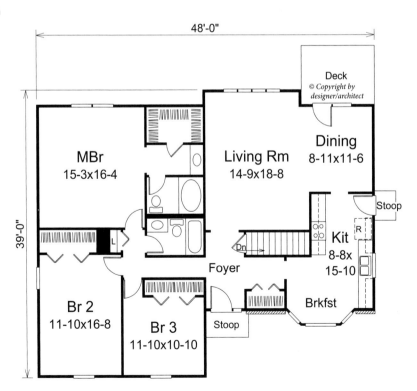

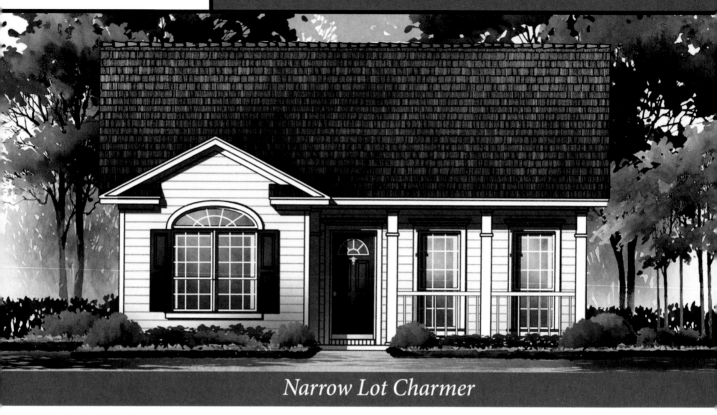

Narrow Lot Charmer

- 1,000 total square feet of living area
- 9' ceilings throughout the house enhance the space
- The open living room offers a gas fireplace flanked by elegant built-in shelves
- The kitchen features a raised bar on each side for serving food to the living room or the breakfast area
- 2 bedrooms, 2 baths
- Slab foundation, drawings also include crawl space foundation

Width: 30'-0"
Depth: 38'-4"

Patio
12-8 x 10

Bedroom #1
11-6 x 13
9' Ceiling

Laun.
5-2 x 6

Breakfast Area
12 x 6
9' Ceiling

Raised Bar

Bath

Jet Tub

Kitchen
12 x 10-4

P

Raised Bar

Clos.

Lin.

Bath

Tub/Shr.

Hall

Living Room
17-6 x 12-11
(Clear)
9' Ceiling

Gas Logs

Built-Ins

Built-Ins

Clos.

Br.

Bedroom #2
11-6 x 13
9' Ceiling

Front Porch
17-10 x 5-0

© Copyright by designer/architect

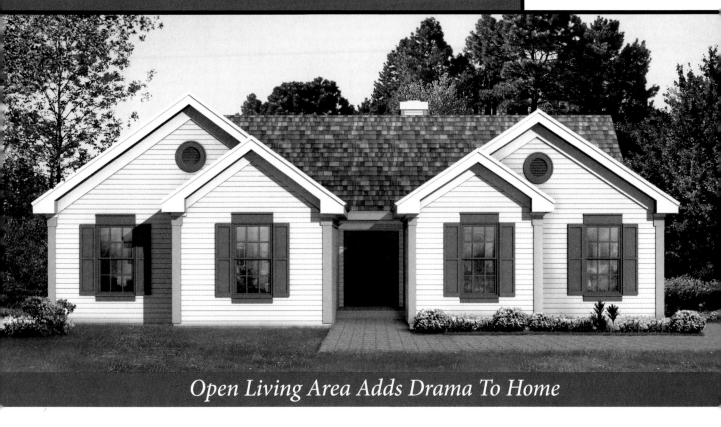

Open Living Area Adds Drama To Home

- 1,340 total square feet of living area
- Master bedroom has a private bath and walk-in closet
- Recessed entry leads to the vaulted family room that shares a see-through fireplace with the kitchen/dining area
- Garage includes a handy storage area
- Convenient laundry closet is located in the kitchen
- 3 bedrooms, 2 baths, 2-car side entry garage
- Slab foundation, drawings also include crawl space foundation

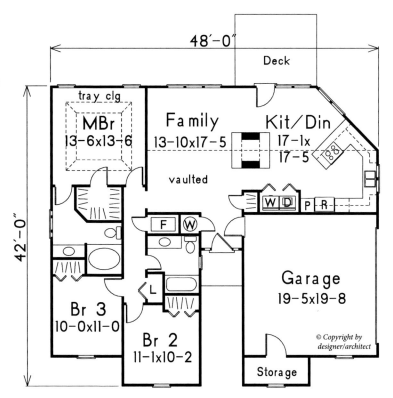

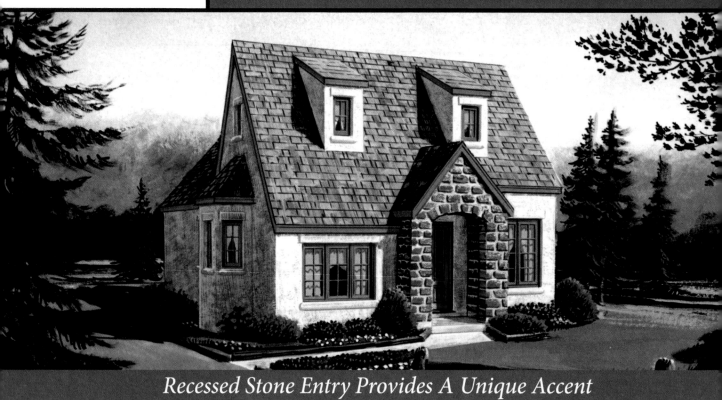

Recessed Stone Entry Provides A Unique Accent

- 717 total square feet of living area
- Incline ladder leads up to a cozy loft area
- The living room features plenty of windows and a vaulted ceiling
- U-shaped kitchen includes a small bay window at the sink
- 1 bedroom, 1 bath
- Slab foundation

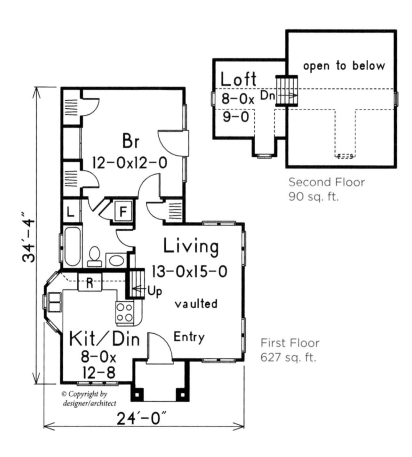

Second Floor
90 sq. ft.

First Floor
627 sq. ft.

© Copyright by designer/architect

Irresistible Retreat

- 448 total square feet of living area
- Bedroom features a large walk-in closet ideal for storage
- Combined dining/sitting area is ideal for relaxing
- Galley-style kitchen is compact and efficient
- Covered porch adds to front facade
- 1 bedroom, 1 bath
- Slab foundation

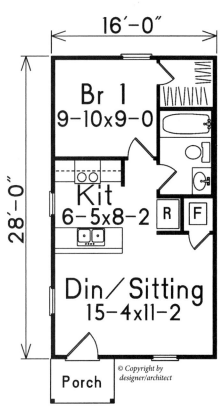

16'-0"

28'-0"

Br 1
9-10x9-0

Kit
6-5x8-2

R F

Din/Sitting
15-4x11-2

© Copyright by
designer/architect

Porch

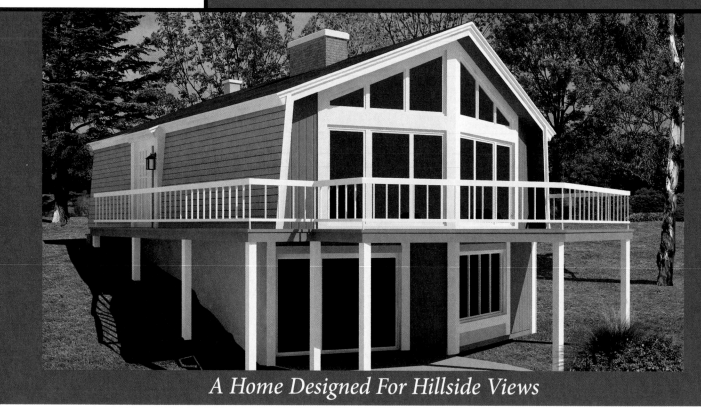

A Home Designed For Hillside Views

- 1,806 total square feet of living area
- Wrap-around deck, great for entertaining, enhances appearance
- Side entry foyer accesses two rear bedrooms, hall bath, and living and dining area
- L-shaped kitchen is open to the dining area
- Lots of living area is provided on the lower level, including a spacious family room with a fireplace and sliding doors to the patio under the deck
- 3 bedrooms, 2 baths
- Walk-out basement foundation

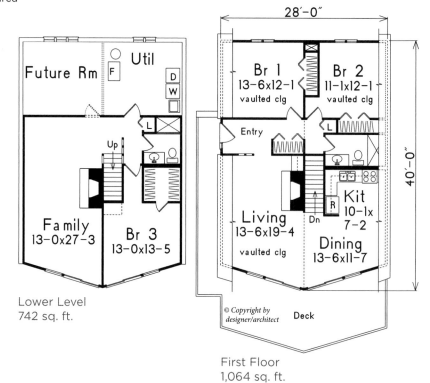

Lower Level
742 sq. ft.

First Floor
1,064 sq. ft.

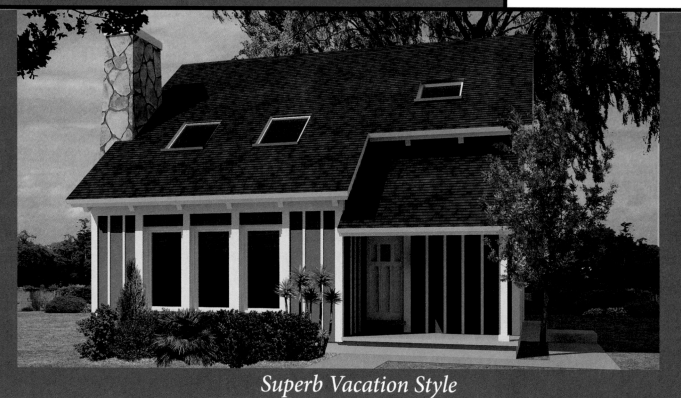

Superb Vacation Style

- 1,278 total square feet of living area
- Energy efficient home with 2" x 6" exterior walls
- Enter this home to find a two-story great room topped with skylights that offer a dramatic first impression
- The screened porch extends dining opportunities and provides a lovely space to enjoy the outdoors year round
- The second floor master bedroom includes a private deck for the ultimate in relaxation
- 2 bedrooms, 1 1/2 baths
- Basement foundation

Second Floor
518 sq. ft.

First Floor
760 sq. ft.

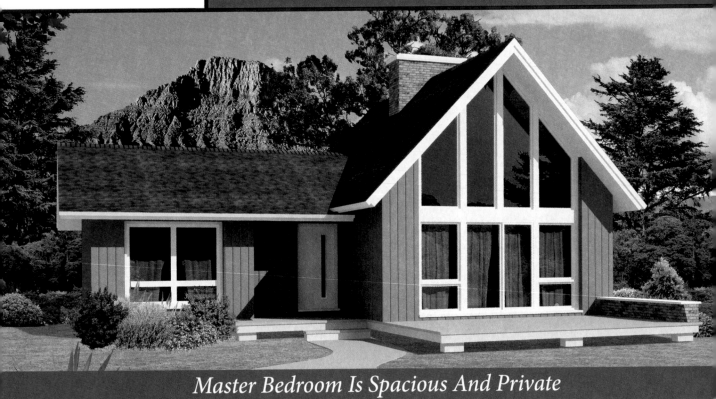

Master Bedroom Is Spacious And Private

- 1,160 total square feet of living area
- Kitchen/dining area combines with the laundry area creating a functional and organized space
- Spacious vaulted living area has a large fireplace and is brightened by glass doors accessing the large deck
- Ascend to the second floor loft by spiral stairs and find a cozy hideaway
- Master bedroom is brightened by many windows and includes a private bath and double closets
- 1 bedroom, 1 bath
- Crawl space foundation

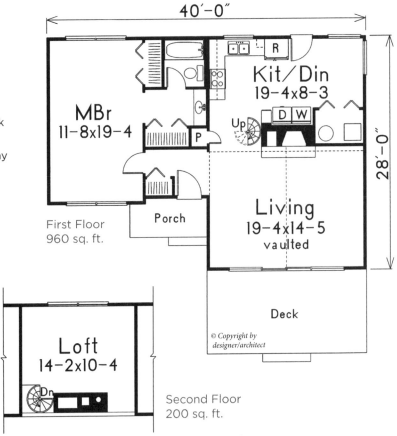

40'-0"

28'-0"

MBr
11-8x19-4

Kit/Din
19-4x8-3

Up

D W

P

Living
19-4x14-5
vaulted

First Floor
960 sq. ft.

Porch

Deck

© Copyright by
designer/architect

Loft
14-2x10-4

Dn

Second Floor
200 sq. ft.

Ornate Corner Porch Catches The Eye

- 1,550 total square feet of living area
- Impressive front entrance with a wrap-around covered porch and raised foyer
- Corner fireplace provides a focal point in the vaulted great room
- Loft is easily converted to a third bedroom or activity center
- Large kitchen/family room includes greenhouse windows and access to the deck and utility area
- The secondary bedroom has a large dormer and window seat
- 2 bedrooms, 2 1/2 baths, 2-car garage
- Basement foundation

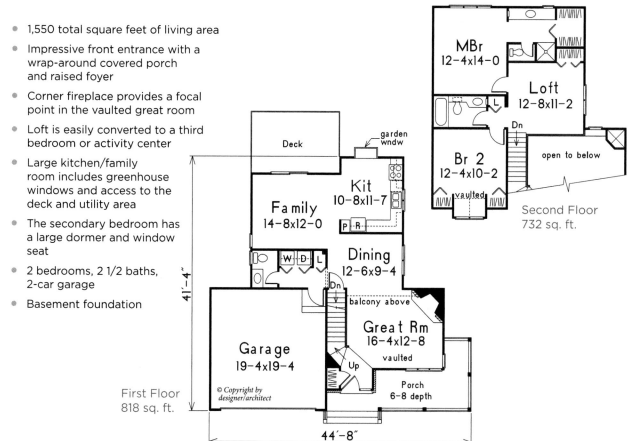

Second Floor
732 sq. ft.

MBr
12-4x14-0

Loft
12-8x11-2

Br 2
12-4x10-2

open to below

vaulted

First Floor
818 sq. ft.

Deck

garden wndw

Kit
10-8x11-7

Family
14-8x12-0

Dining
12-6x9-4

W·D·L

P·R

Dn

balcony above

Garage
19-4x19-4

Great Rm
16-4x12-8
vaulted

Up

Porch
6-8 depth

© Copyright by designer/architect

41'-4"

44'-8"

Family Living Focuses Around Central Fireplace

- 1,388 total square feet of living area
- Handsome see-through fireplace offers a gathering point for the kitchen, family and breakfast rooms
- Vaulted ceiling and large bay window in the master bedroom add charm to this room
- A dramatic angular wall and large windows add brightness to the kitchen and breakfast room
- Kitchen, breakfast and family rooms have vaulted ceilings, adding spaciousness to this central living area
- 3 bedrooms, 2 baths, 2-car garage
- Crawl space foundation, drawings also include slab foundation

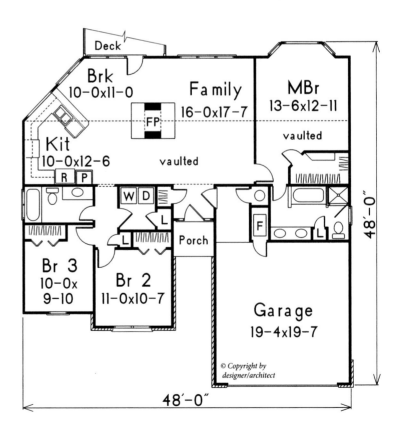

Affordable Simplicity

- 1,196 total square feet of living area

- Home includes an extra-deep porch for evening relaxation

- The large living room enjoys a corner fireplace, dining area featuring a wide bay window with sliding doors to the rear patio, and a snack bar open to the kitchen

- The master bedroom has a nice walk-in closet, its own linen closet and a roomy bath with a double-bowl vanity and garden tub

- 3 bedrooms, 2 baths, 1-car side entry garage

- Crawl space foundation, drawings also include slab foundation

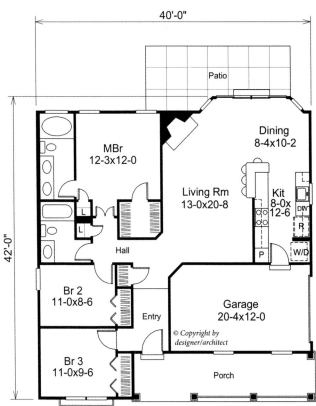

Surrounding Porch For Country Views

- 1,428 total square feet of living area

- Large vaulted family room opens to the dining area and kitchen with breakfast bar

- First floor master bedroom offers a large bath, walk-in closet and nearby laundry facilities

- A spacious loft/bedroom #3 overlooking the family room and an additional bedroom and bath complement the second floor

- 2" x 6" exterior walls available, please order plan #539-058D-0080

- 3 bedrooms, 2 baths

- Basement foundation

Second Floor
415 sq. ft.

Loft/
Br 3
10-7x11-11

Open To Below

Dn

L

Br 2
12-8x10-0

46'-0"

42'-6"

Kit
11-3x12-0

Dining
10-7x12-0

D

W

L

Dn

Family
14-11x15-6

Up

MBr
12-8x14-0

© Copyright by
designer/architect

Covered Porch
depth 7-0

First Floor
1,013 sq. ft.

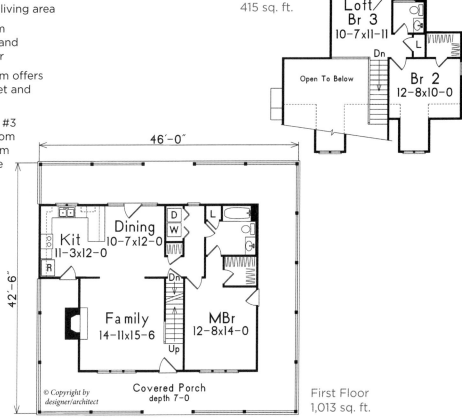

Cozy Vacation Retreat

- 1,391 total square feet of living area
- Large living room with masonry fireplace features a soaring vaulted ceiling
- A spiral staircase in the hall leads to a huge sleeping loft overlooking the living room below
- Two first floor bedrooms share a full bath
- 2 bedrooms, 1 bath
- Pier foundation, drawings also include crawl space foundation

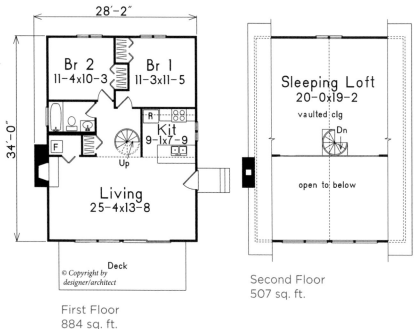

28'-2"

34'-0"

Br 2
11-4x10-3

Br 1
11-3x11-5

Kit
9-1x7-9

Up

Living
25-4x13-8

Deck

© Copyright by
designer/architect

First Floor
884 sq. ft.

Sleeping Loft
20-0x19-2
vaulted clg

Dn

open to below

Second Floor
507 sq. ft.

Compact And Efficient

- 1,384 total square feet of living area
- The entry leads into the large vaulted family room that enjoys a corner fireplace and access to the rear yard
- The U-shaped kitchen has an abundance of counterspace and opens to the bayed dining room
- Split bedrooms ensure privacy for all
- 3 bedrooms, 2 baths, 2-car garage
- Slab foundation

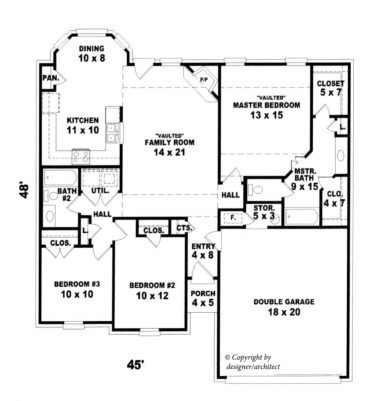

Innovative Design For That Narrow Lot

- 1,558 total square feet of living area
- Illuminated spaces are created by visual access to the outdoor living areas
- Vaulted master bedroom features a private bath with whirlpool tub, separate shower and large walk-in closet
- Convenient laundry area has garage access
- Practical den or third bedroom is perfect for a variety of uses
- U-shaped kitchen is adjacent to the sunny breakfast area
- 2 bedrooms, 2 baths, 2-car rear entry garage
- Basement foundation

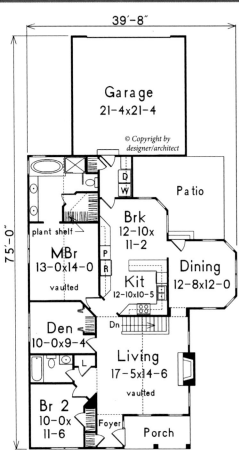

Elegant Home With Unique Entry Courtyard

- 1,693 total square feet of living area

- The perfect starter home, vacation getaway or residence for empty-nesters

- Decorative columns with lanterns, door and window trim with custom grilles and a dressy roof dormer define this state-of-the-art exterior

- The living room enjoys a fireplace with flanking glass doors to an oversized rear patio and a dining area with bay window

- A pass-through snack counter is part of the smartly-designed kitchen that features an abundance of cabinets, built-in pantry and convenient adjacent laundry room

- The spacious master bedroom has an elegant bath, large walk-in closet and 9' wide sliding glass doors to the rear patio

- 2 bedrooms, 2 baths, 2-car garage

- Crawl space foundation, drawings also include slab foundation

Terrific Cottage-Style Design

- 1,922 total square feet of living area
- Master bedroom includes many luxuries such as an oversized private bath and large walk-in closet
- The kitchen is spacious with a functional eat-in breakfast bar and is adjacent to the nook which is ideal as a breakfast room
- Plenty of storage is featured in both bedrooms on the second floor and in the hall
- Enormous utility room is centrally located on the first floor
- 3 bedrooms, 2 1/2 baths
- Basement foundation

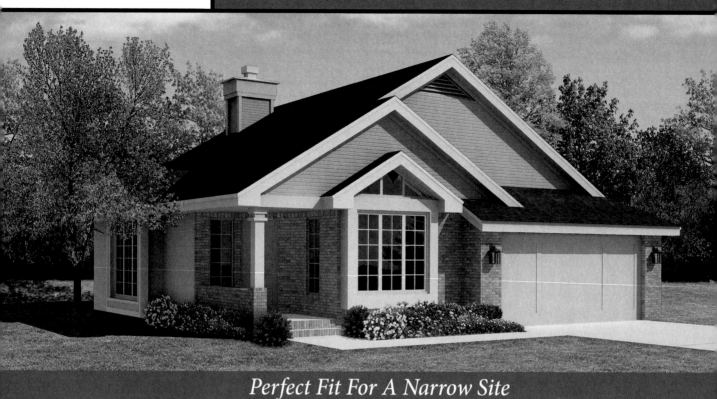

Perfect Fit For A Narrow Site

- 1,270 total square feet of living area
- Spacious living area features angled stairs, vaulted ceiling, exciting fireplace and deck access
- Master bedroom includes a walk-in closet and private bath
- Dining and living rooms join to create an open atmosphere
- Eat-in kitchen has a convenient pass-through to the dining room
- 3 bedrooms, 2 baths, 2-car garage
- Basement foundation

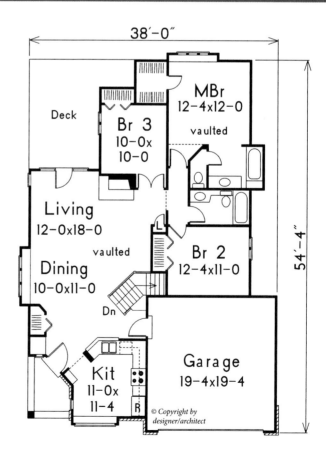

38'-0"

54'-4"

Deck

Br 3
10-0x
10-0

MBr
12-4x12-0
vaulted

Living
12-0x18-0
vaulted

Dining
10-0x11-0

Br 2
12-4x11-0

Dn

Kit
11-0x
11-4

Garage
19-4x19-4

© Copyright by designer/architect

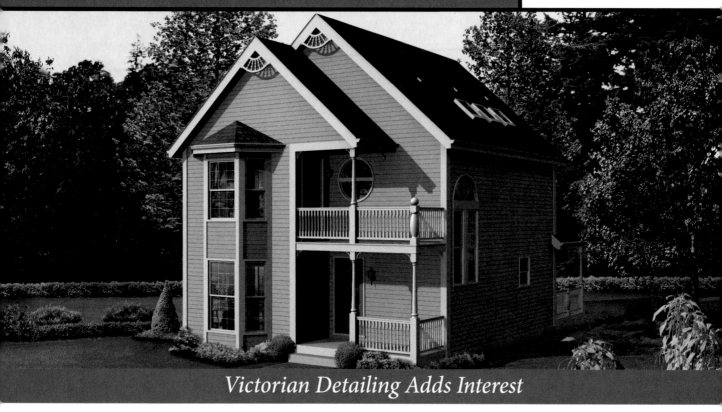

Victorian Detailing Adds Interest

- 1,662 total square feet of living area
- The family room is an ideal place for casual family gatherings
- Well-organized kitchen includes lots of storage space, a walk-in pantry and plenty of cabinetry
- The rear of the home features a versatile back porch for dining or relaxing
- Master bedroom has a bay window and private balcony
- 2 bedrooms, 1 1/2 baths
- Basement foundation

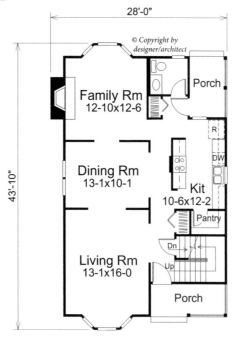

First Floor
1,092 sq. ft.

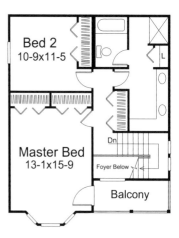

Second Floor
570 sq. ft.

Three Bedroom Luxury In A Small Home

- 1,161 total square feet of living area
- Brickwork and feature window add elegance to this home for a narrow lot
- Living room enjoys a vaulted ceiling, fireplace and opens to the kitchen
- U-shaped kitchen offers a breakfast area with bay window, snack bar and built-in pantry
- 3 bedrooms, 2 baths
- Basement foundation

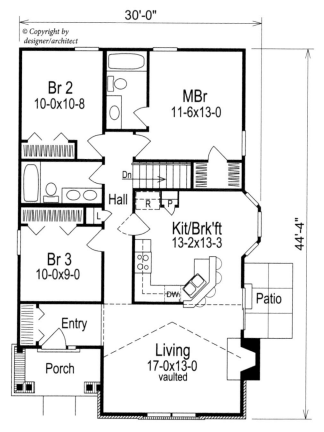

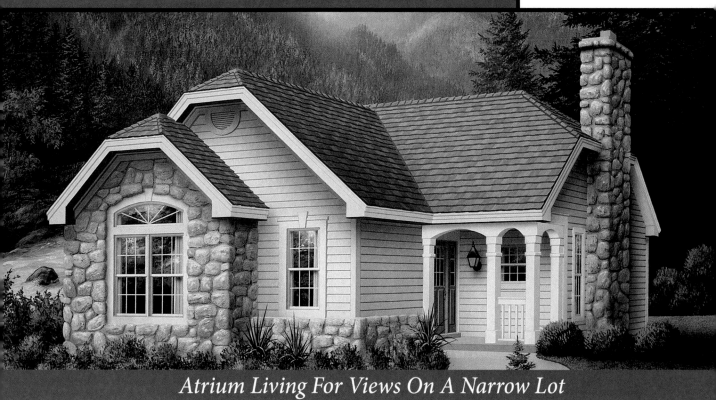

Atrium Living For Views On A Narrow Lot

- 1,231 total square feet of living area
- Dutch gables and stone accents provide an enchanting appearance
- The spacious living room offers a masonry fireplace, atrium with window wall and is open to a dining area with bay window
- Kitchen has a breakfast counter, lots of cabinet space and glass sliding doors to a balcony
- 380 square feet of optional living area on the lower level
- 2 bedrooms, 2 baths, 1-car drive under rear entry garage
- Walk-out basement foundation

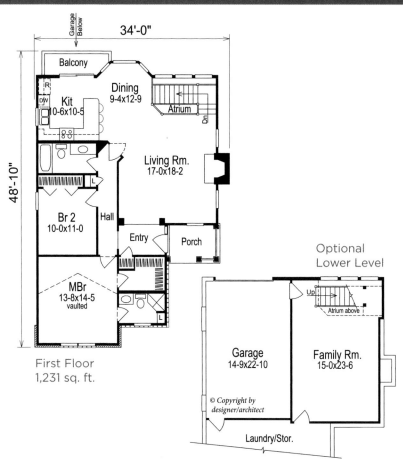

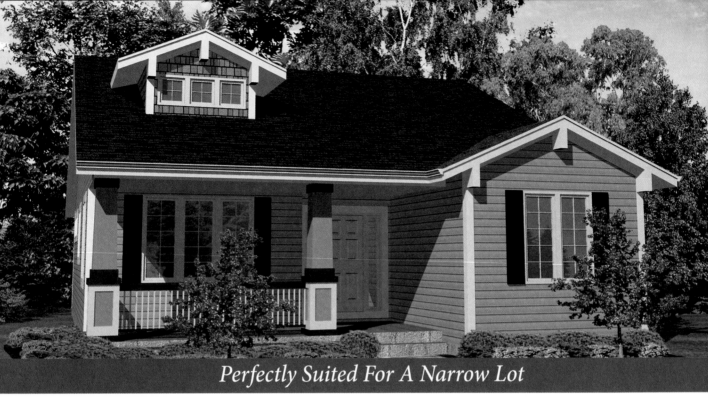

Perfectly Suited For A Narrow Lot

- 1,800 total square feet of living area

- This Craftsman style home features a stylish exterior and amenity-full interior

- Cheerful and bright, the family room is the perfect place to relax and will no doubt be the center of activity

- Substantial closet space can be found in the remotely located master bedroom

- 3 bedrooms, 2 baths, 2-car rear entry garage

- Basement foundation

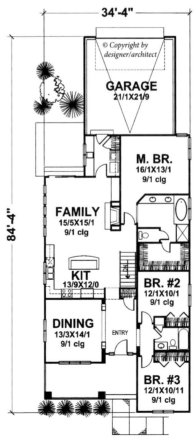

Efficient Ranch With Country Charm

- 1,364 total square feet of living area
- Master bedroom features a spacious walk-in closet and private bath
- Living room is highlighted with several windows
- Kitchen with snack bar is adjacent to the dining area
- Plenty of storage space throughout
- 3 bedrooms, 2 baths, optional 2-car garage
- Basement foundation, drawings also include crawl space foundation

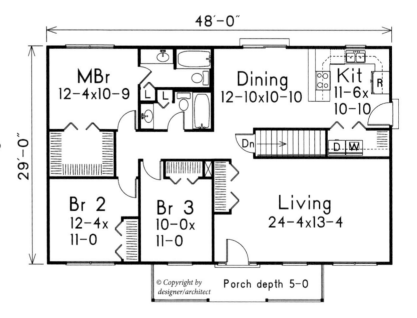

48'-0"

29'-0"

MBr
12-4x10-9

Dining
12-10x10-10

Kit
11-6x
10-10

Dn

D W

Br 2
12-4x
11-0

Br 3
10-0x
11-0

Living
24-4x13-4

© Copyright by designer/architect

Porch depth 5-0

Gable Facade Adds Appeal To This Ranch

- 1,304 total square feet of living area
- Covered entrance leads into the family room with a cozy fireplace
- 10' ceilings in the kitchen, dining and family rooms
- Master bedroom features a coffered ceiling, walk-in closet and private bath
- Efficient kitchen includes large window over the sink
- 3 bedrooms, 2 baths, 2-car garage
- Slab foundation

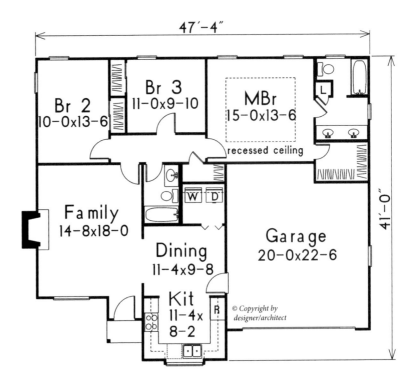

47'-4"

Br 2
10-0x13-6

Br 3
11-0x9-10

MBr
15-0x13-6
recessed ceiling

Family
14-8x18-0

W D

Dining
11-4x9-8

Garage
20-0x22-6

Kit
11-4x
8-2

© Copyright by designer/architect

41'-0"

Elegance In A Starter Or Retirement Home

- 888 total square feet of living area
- Home features an eye-catching exterior and has a spacious porch
- The breakfast room with bay window is open to the living room and adjoins the kitchen with pass-through snack bar
- The bedrooms are quite roomy and feature walk-in closets
- The master bedroom has a double-door entry and access to the rear patio
- 2 bedrooms, 1 bath, 1-car garage
- Basement foundation

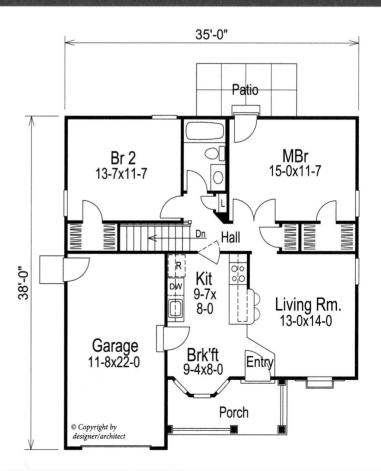

Master Bath Has Elegant Features

- 1,974 total square feet of living area
- Breakfast room with full windows blends into the family room
- Second floor includes private master bedroom suite and easy access to laundry facility
- Elegant master bath has a large corner tub with separate shower and vanities
- Traditional entrance framed by a covered porch and sidelights
- 3 bedrooms, 2 1/2 baths, 2-car drive under garage
- Basement foundation

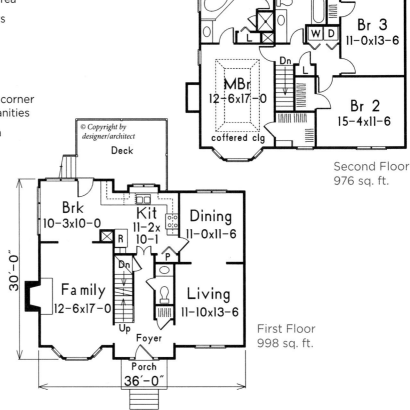

Second Floor
976 sq. ft.

Br 3
11-0x13-6

Br 2
15-4x11-6

MBr
12-6x17-0

coffered clg

© Copyright by
designer/architect

Deck

Brk
10-3x10-0

Kit
11-2x10-1

Dining
11-0x11-6

Family
12-6x17-0

Living
11-10x13-6

30'-0"

Foyer

Porch
36'-0"

First Floor
998 sq. ft.

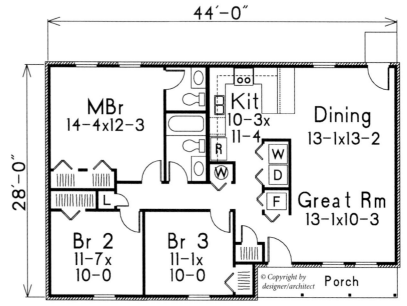

Large Great Room And Dining Area

- 1,160 total square feet of living area

- U-shaped kitchen has breakfast bar and convenient laundry closet

- Master bedroom has private half bath and large closet

- Dining room features handy access to the outdoors

- Open living atmosphere is created by the adjoining dining area and great room

- 3 bedrooms, 1 1/2 baths

- Crawl space foundation, drawings also include basement and slab foundations

44'-0"

28'-0"

MBr
14-4x12-3

Kit
10-3x
11-4

Dining
13-1x13-2

R

W

W
D
F

Great Rm
13-1x10-3

L

Br 2
11-7x
10-0

Br 3
11-1x
10-0

© Copyright by
designer/architect

Porch

A Vacation Oasis

- 1,106 total square feet of living area
- Delightful A-frame provides exciting vacation-style living all year long
- Deck accesses a large living room with an open soaring ceiling
- Enormous sleeping area is provided on the second floor with balcony overlook to living room below
- 2 bedrooms, 1 bath
- Pier foundation

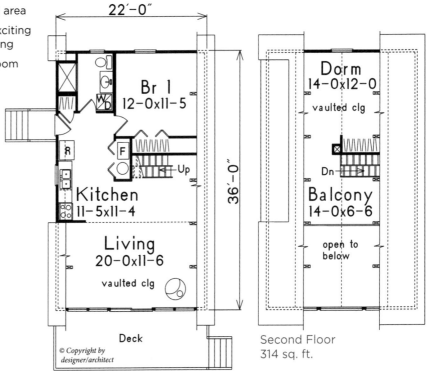

22'-0"

Br 1
12-0x11-5

36'-0"

Kitchen
11-5x11-4

Living
20-0x11-6
vaulted clg

Up

Deck

© Copyright by
designer/architect

First Floor
792 sq. ft.

Dorm
14-0x12-0
vaulted clg

Dn

Balcony
14-0x6-6

open to
below

Second Floor
314 sq. ft.

Charming Window Box Adds Curb Appeal

- 1,621 total square feet of living area
- 18' ceilings in the living and dining areas add spaciousness
- All bedrooms feature walk-in closets
- Bonus room on the second floor has an additional 257 square feet of living area
- 3 bedrooms, 2 1/2 baths, 2-car garage
- Basement foundation, drawings also include crawl space foundation

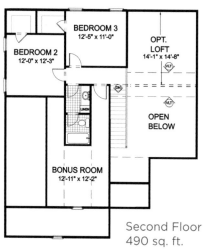

Second Floor
490 sq. ft.

First Floor
1,131 sq. ft.

Delightful Country Cabin

- 953 total square feet of living area
- Relax on porches fit for charming rocking chairs
- With two large bedrooms that feature oversized closets, a spacious kitchen and a family room with a fireplace, this home has everything you need to enjoy a vacation getaway
- The kitchen has a sunny corner double sink, roomy center island/snack bar and shares a vaulted ceiling with the family room
- 2 bedrooms, 1 1/2 baths
- Crawl space foundation

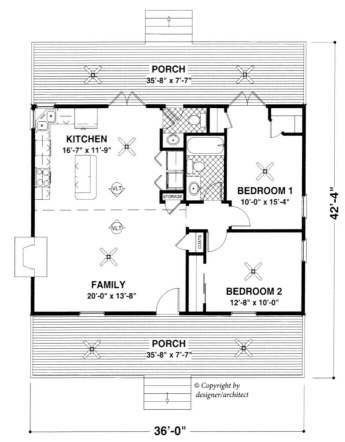

PORCH
35'-8" x 7'-7"

KITCHEN
16'-7" x 11'-9"

STORAGE

VLT

VLT

BEDROOM 1
10'-0" x 15'-4"

COATS

FAMILY
20'-0" x 13'-8"

BEDROOM 2
12'-8" x 10'-0"

42'-4"

PORCH
35'-8" x 7'-7"

© Copyright by designer/architect

36'-0"

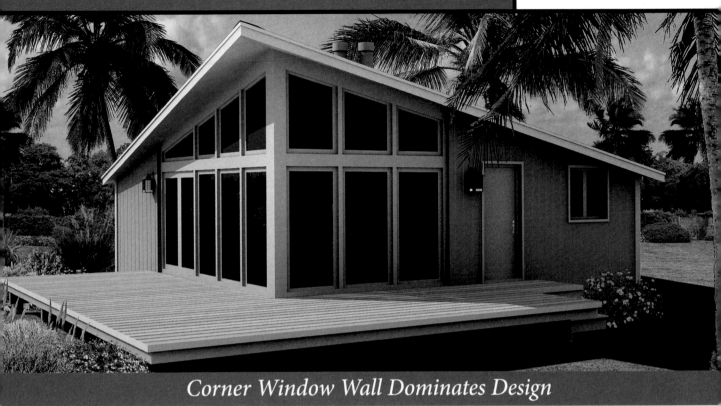

Corner Window Wall Dominates Design

- 784 total square feet of living area
- Outdoor relaxation will be enjoyed with this home's huge wrap-around wood deck
- Upon entering the spacious living area, a cozy free-standing fireplace, sloped ceiling and corner window wall catch the eye
- Charming kitchen features pass-through peninsula to dining area
- 3 bedrooms, 1 bath
- Pier foundation

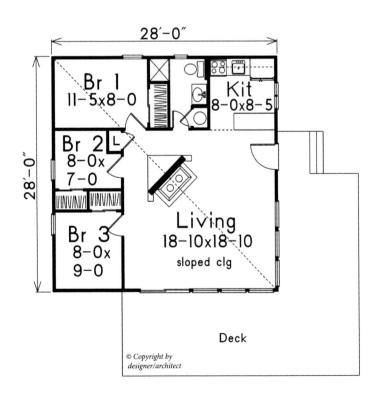

28'-0"

28'-0"

Br 1
11-5x8-0

Kit
8-0x8-5

Br 2
8-0x
7-0

Br 3
8-0x
9-0

Living
18-10x18-10
sloped clg

Deck

© Copyright by
designer/architect

Country Retreat For Quiet Times

- 1,211 total square feet of living area

- Extraordinary views are enjoyed in the vaulted family room through sliding doors

- The functional kitchen features a snack bar and laundry closet

- Bedroom and bunk room complete the first floor while a large bedroom with two storage areas and balcony complete the second floor

- Plan also includes an alternate second floor with a third bedroom and 223 additional square feet of living space

- 2 bedrooms, 1 bath

- Crawl space foundation, drawings also include basement foundation

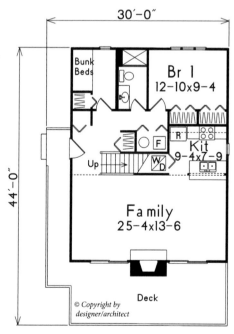

First Floor
884 sq. ft.

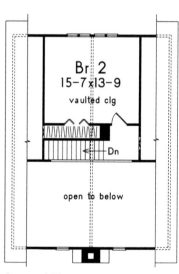

Second Floor
327 sq. ft.

Cozy Ranch Home

- 950 total square feet of living area
- The deck is attached to the kitchen, perfect for outdoor dining
- Vaulted ceiling, open stairway and fireplace complement the great room
- Bedroom #2 with a sloped ceiling and box-bay window can be converted to a den
- Master bedroom has a walk-in closet, plant shelf, separate dressing area and private access to the bath
- Kitchen has garage access and opens to the great room
- 2 bedrooms, 1 bath, 1-car garage
- Basement foundation

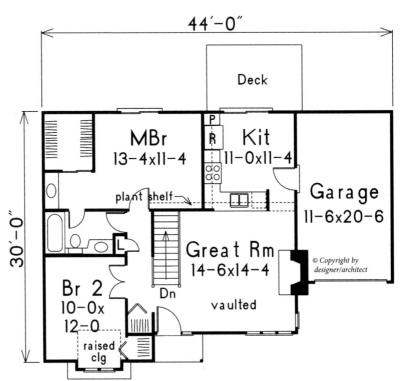

Begging For A Country Setting

- 1,293 total square feet of living area
- A very affordable ranch home that's easy to build
- Living room has separate entry, guest closet and opens to the dining area
- Eat-in L-shaped kitchen offers a pass-through to the family room
- Master bedroom has its own bath and large walk-in closet
- 3 bedrooms, 2 baths, 1-car garage
- Basement foundation, drawings also include crawl space foundation

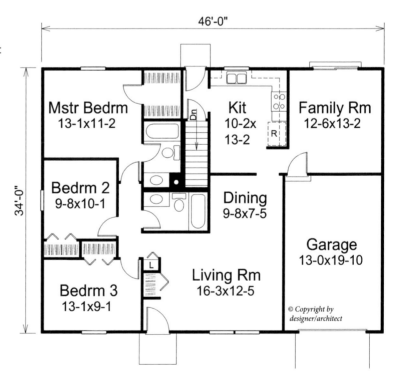

46'-0"

34'-0"

Mstr Bedrm
13-1x11-2

Kit
10-2x
13-2

Family Rm
12-6x13-2

Bedrm 2
9-8x10-1

Dining
9-8x7-5

Bedrm 3
13-1x9-1

Living Rm
16-3x12-5

Garage
13-0x19-10

© Copyright by designer/architect

Dormers Accent Country Home

- 1,818 total square feet of living area
- The breakfast room is tucked behind the kitchen and has a laundry closet and deck access
- Living and dining areas share a vaulted ceiling and fireplace
- Master bedroom has two closets, a large double-bowl vanity and a separate tub and shower
- Large front porch wraps around the home
- 4 bedrooms, 2 1/2 baths, 2-car drive under side entry garage
- Walk-out basement foundation

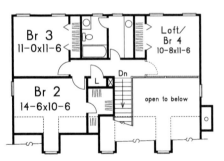

Second Floor
686 sq. ft.

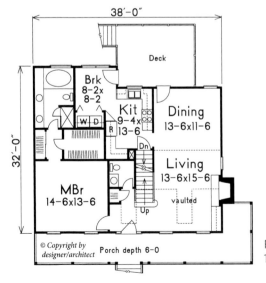

First Floor
1,132 sq. ft.

L-Shaped Kitchen Joined With Dining Area

- 1,000 total square feet of living area
- Master bedroom has double closets and an adjacent bath
- L-shaped kitchen includes side entrance, closet and convenient laundry area
- Living room features handy coat closet
- 3 bedrooms, 1 bath
- Crawl space foundation, drawings also include basement and slab foundations

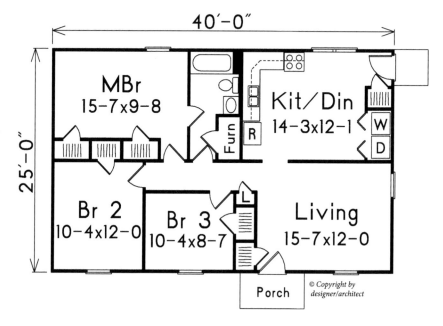

40'-0"

25'-0"

MBr
15-7x9-8

Furn

Kit/Din
14-3x12-1

R

W
D

Br 2
10-4x12-0

Br 3
10-4x8-7

Living
15-7x12-0

Porch

© Copyright by designer/architect

Efficient Split Level, Nice Privacy

- 1,680 total square feet of living area
- Country facade and covered front porch
- Large basement area for family room, study or hobby area
- Plenty of closet space throughout this design
- 3 bedrooms, 2 baths, 2-car garage
- Partial basement/crawl space foundation

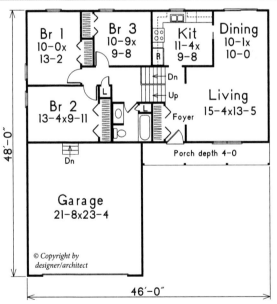

First Floor
1,104 sq. ft.

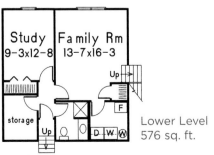

Lower Level
576 sq. ft.

Luxury Home For Narrow Site Has Exciting Interior

- 2,158 total square feet of living area
- Vaulted entry has a coat closet and built-in shelves with plant shelf above
- The two-story living room has tall dramatic windows flanking the fireplace and a full-length second floor balcony
- A laundry and half bath are located near the kitchen which has over 30' of counterspace
- Vaulted master bedroom has window seat entry, two walk-in closets and a luxury bath
- 3 bedrooms, 2 1/2 baths, 2-car garage
- Basement foundation

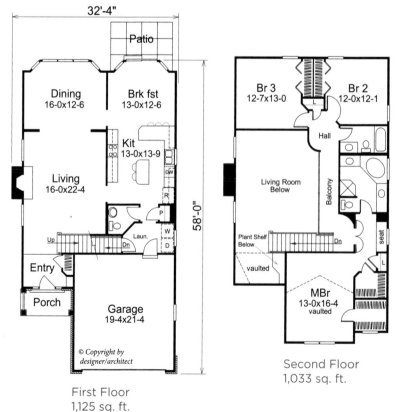

First Floor
1,125 sq. ft.

Second Floor
1,033 sq. ft.

Covered Porch Surrounds Home

- 1,399 total square feet of living area
- Living room overlooks the dining area through arched columns
- Laundry room contains a handy half bath
- Spacious master bedroom includes a sitting area, walk-in closet and plenty of sunlight
- 3 bedrooms, 1 1/2 baths, 1-car garage
- Basement foundation, drawings also include crawl space and slab foundations

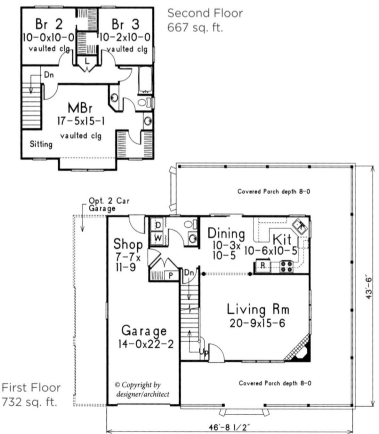

Second Floor
667 sq. ft.

Br 2
10-0x10-0
vaulted clg

Br 3
10-2x10-0
vaulted clg

Dn

MBr
17-5x15-1
vaulted clg

Sitting

Opt. 2 Car Garage

Covered Porch depth 8-0

Shop
7-7x
11-9

Dining
10-3x
10-5

Kit
10-6x10-5

Garage
14-0x22-2

Living Rm
20-9x15-6

Dn

Up

© Copyright by designer/architect

Covered Porch depth 8-0

First Floor
732 sq. ft.

43'-6"

46'-8 1/2"

Appealing Charming Porch

- 1,643 total square feet of living area
- First floor master bedroom has a private bath, walk-in closet and easy access to the laundry closet
- Comfortable family room features a vaulted ceiling and a cozy fireplace
- Two bedrooms on the second floor share a bath
- 3 bedrooms, 2 1/2 baths, 2-car drive under side entry garage
- Basement or crawl space foundation, please specify when ordering

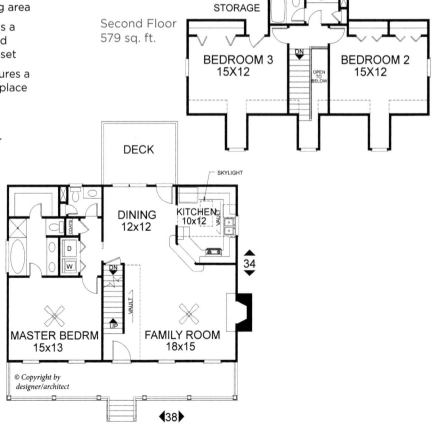

Second Floor
579 sq. ft.

STORAGE

BEDROOM 3
15X12

OPEN TO BELOW

BEDROOM 2
15X12

DECK

SKYLIGHT

DINING
12x12

KITCHEN
10x12

34

MASTER BEDRM
15x13

FAMILY ROOM
18x15

© Copyright by designer/architect

First Floor
1,064 sq. ft.

38

Gabled, Covered Front Porch

- 1,320 total square feet of living area
- Functional U-shaped kitchen features a pantry
- Large living and dining areas join to create an open atmosphere
- Secluded master bedroom includes a private full bath
- Covered front porch opens into a large living area with a convenient coat closet
- Utility/laundry room is located near the kitchen
- 3 bedrooms, 2 baths
- Crawl space foundation

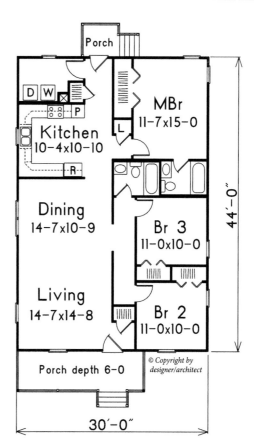

Porch

D W ☒

P

Kitchen
10-4x10-10

R

MBr
11-7x15-0

L

Dining
14-7x10-9

Br 3
11-0x10-0

Living
14-7x14-8

Br 2
11-0x10-0

44'-0"

Porch depth 6-0

© Copyright by designer/architect

30'-0"

Perfect Design For A Narrow Lot

- 1,112 total square feet of living area
- Energy efficient home with 2" x 6" exterior walls
- Brick, an arched window and planter box decorate the facade of this lovely ranch home
- The eat-in kitchen offers an abundance of counterspace and enjoys access to the outdoors
- Three bedrooms are situated together for easy family living
- 3 bedrooms, 1 bath
- Basement foundation

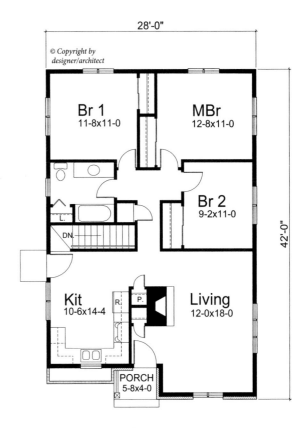

© Copyright by designer/architect

28'-0"

42'-0"

Br 1
11-8x11-0

MBr
12-8x11-0

Br 2
9-2x11-0

DN.

L.

Kit
10-6x14-4

R.

P.

Living
12-0x18-0

PORCH
5-8x4-0

Great Room's Symmetry Steals The Show

- 1,985 total square feet of living area

- Charming design for a narrow lot

- Dramatic sunken great room features a vaulted ceiling, large double-hung windows and transomed patio doors

- Grand master bedroom includes a double-door entry, large closet, elegant bath and patio access

- 4 bedrooms, 3 1/2 baths, 2-car garage

- Basement foundation

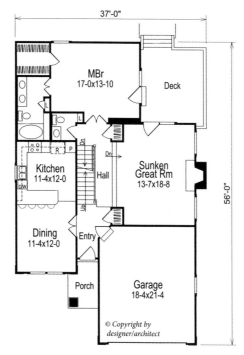

First Floor
1,114 sq. ft.

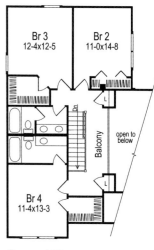

Second Floor
871 sq. ft.

Delightful Split-Level Home

- 999 total square feet of living area

- The dramatic entry is brightened by a glass front door and an arched transom window

- Vaulted ceilings adorn the kitchen, family and dining rooms providing a feeling of spaciousness

- A future studio on the lower level has an additional 300 square feet of living area and features a bath and a kitchenette making it ideal for a college student or in-law

- 2 bedrooms, 2 baths, 2-car garage

- Basement foundation

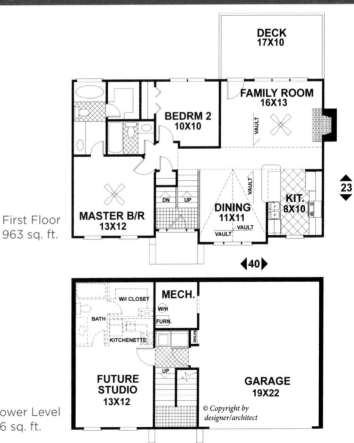

First Floor
963 sq. ft.

Lower Level
36 sq. ft.

© Copyright by designer/architect

Inviting Craftsman Home

- 1,800 total square feet of living area
- The open kitchen flows nicely into the bayed dining room for a spacious, cheerful setting
- Enjoy outdoor meals on the rear covered porch that comes equipped with an outdoor kitchen
- An oversized laundry room and unique flex space add extra storage area for the growing family
- 3 bedrooms, 2 baths, 2-car side entry garage
- Slab foundation, drawings also include crawl space foundation

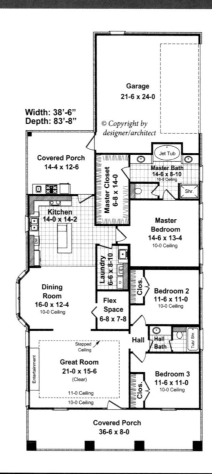

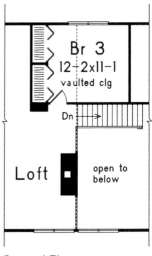

Large Windows Brighten Home Inside And Out

- 1,260 total square feet of living area
- Living area features an enormous stone fireplace and sliding glass doors for accessing the deck
- Kitchen/dining area is organized with lots of cabinet and counterspace
- Second bedroom is vaulted and has closet space along one entire wall
- 3 bedrooms, 1 bath
- Crawl space foundation

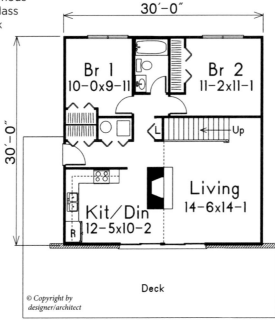

30'-0"

30'-0"

Br 1
10-0x9-11

Br 2
11-2x11-1

Up

Kit/Din
12-5x10-2

Living
14-6x14-1

© Copyright by
designer/architect

Deck

First Floor
900 sq. ft.

Br 3
12-2x11-1
vaulted clg

Dn

Loft

open to
below

Second Floor
360 sq. ft.

Bright, Spacious And Appealing

- 1,835 total square feet of living area
- The arched entry and vaulted foyer create a welcoming appearance
- Divided dining and living rooms continue with vaulted ceilings to provide a distinguished openness
- Country kitchen with cozy fireplace and greenhouse windows offers a central gathering area
- Open stairway overlooks foyer
- All bedrooms are located on the second floor for added privacy
- 3 bedrooms, 2 1/2 baths, 2-car garage
- Basement foundation

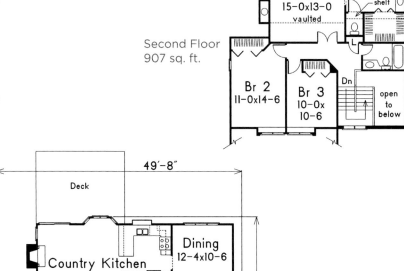

Second Floor
907 sq. ft.

First Floor
928 sq. ft.

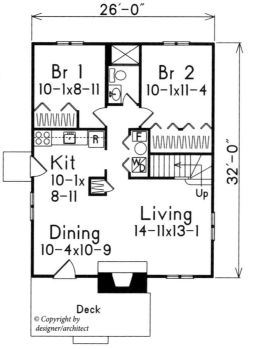

Cozy Cottage Living

- 1,280 total square feet of living area
- A front porch deck, ornate porch roof, massive stone fireplace and Old-English windows all generate an inviting appearance
- The large living room accesses the kitchen and spacious dining area
- Two spacious bedrooms with ample closet space comprise the second floor
- 4 bedrooms, 2 baths
- Basement foundation, drawings also include crawl space foundation

26'-0"

Br 1
10-1x8-11

Br 2
10-1x11-4

32'-0"

Kit
10-1x
8-11

Living
14-11x13-1

Up

Dining
10-4x10-9

Deck
© Copyright by
designer/architect

First Floor
832 sq. ft.

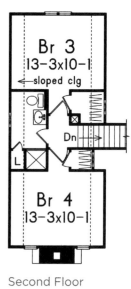

Br 3
13-3x10-1
←sloped clg

Dn

Br 4
13-3x10-1

Second Floor
448 sq. ft.

Roughing It In Luxury

- 1,200 total square feet of living area
- Ornate ranch-style railing enhances the exterior while the stone fireplace provides a visual anchor
- Spectacular living room features an inviting fireplace and adjoins a charming kitchen with dining area
- Two second floor bedrooms share a half bath
- 3 bedrooms, 1 1/2 baths
- Crawl space foundation, drawings also include slab foundation

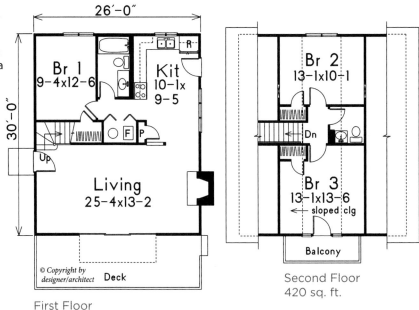

First Floor
780 sq. ft.

Second Floor
420 sq. ft.

Sophisticated Efficiency

- 1,508 total square feet of living area
- Contemporary facade enhances appeal
- Vaulted ceilings and openness of living and dining rooms deliver spaciousness
- Kitchen has access to outdoors or an optional two-car garage
- Second floor bedrooms share a large bath with double-bowl vanity and skylight
- 4 bedrooms, 2 baths, optional 2-car garage
- Basement foundation, drawings also include crawl space and slab foundations

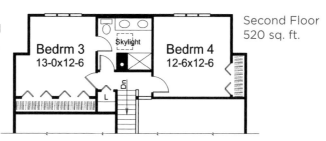

Second Floor
520 sq. ft.

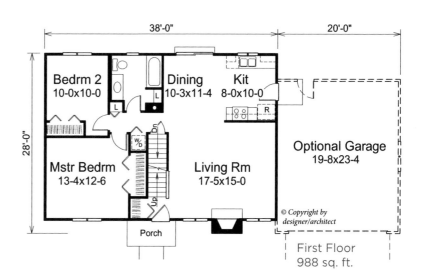

First Floor
988 sq. ft.

LOWE'S LEGACY SERIES

Vaulted Living Area With Corner Fireplace

- 1,448 total square feet of living area
- Dining room conveniently adjoins kitchen and accesses rear deck
- Private first floor master bedroom
- Secondary bedrooms share a bath and cozy loft area
- 3 bedrooms, 2 1/2 baths, 2-car garage
- Basement foundation

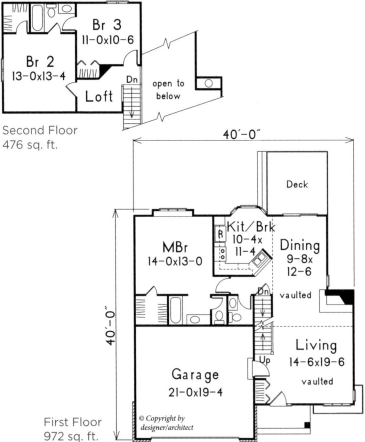

Second Floor
476 sq. ft.

Br 2
13-0x13-4

Br 3
11-0x10-6

Loft

Dn

open to below

First Floor
972 sq. ft.

40'-0"

40'-0"

Deck

MBr
14-0x13-0

Kit/Brk
10-4x
11-4

Dining
9-8x
12-6

vaulted

Dn

Living
14-6x19-6

vaulted

Up

Garage
21-0x19-4

© Copyright by designer/architect

Handsome, Compact Ranch

- 1,296 total square feet of living area

- Two secondary bedrooms share a bath and have convenient access to the laundry room

- Family room has a large fireplace flanked by sunny windows

- Master bedroom includes privacy as well as an amenity-full bath

- 3 bedrooms, 2 baths, 2-car garage

- Basement foundation, drawings also include crawl space and slab foundations

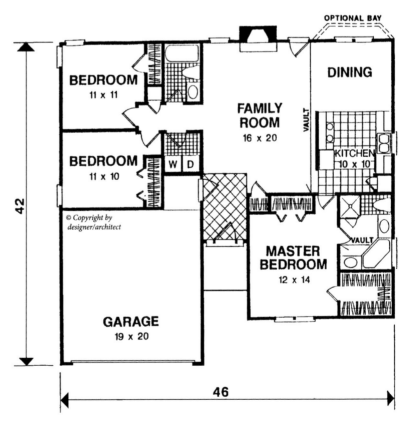

OPTIONAL BAY

BEDROOM
11 x 11

DINING

FAMILY ROOM
16 x 20

VAULT

KITCHEN
10 x 10

BEDROOM
11 x 10

W D

© Copyright by designer/architect

MASTER BEDROOM
12 x 14

VAULT

42

GARAGE
19 x 20

46

Perfect Home For A Small Family

- 864 total square feet of living area
- L-shaped kitchen with convenient pantry is adjacent to dining area
- Easy access to laundry area, linen closet and storage closet
- Both bedrooms include ample closet space
- 2 bedrooms, 1 bath
- Crawl space foundation, drawings also include basement and slab foundations

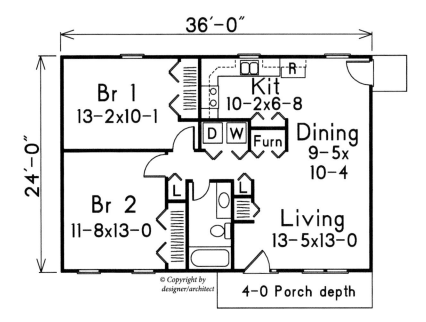

36'-0"

24'-0"

Br 1
13-2x10-1

Kit
10-2x6-8

D W Furn

Dining
9-5x
10-4

Br 2
11-8x13-0

Living
13-5x13-0

© Copyright by
designer/architect

4-0 Porch depth

Efficient Ranch For A Slender Lot

- 1,171 total square feet of living area

- This home is perfect for a starter home, second home on a lake or countryside setting

- The vaulted living room offers many exciting features including a corner fireplace and dining area with sliding doors to the side patio

- A built-in pantry, vaulted ceiling and breakfast bar are just a few amenities of the delightful kitchen

- 3 bedrooms, 2 baths, 2-car garage

- Basement foundation, drawings also include slab and crawl space foundations

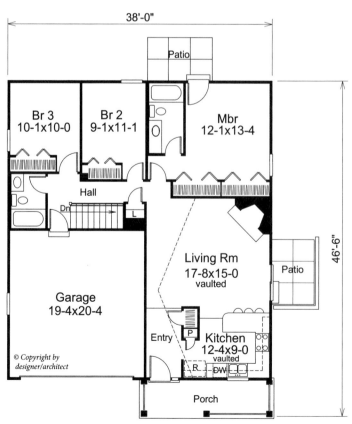

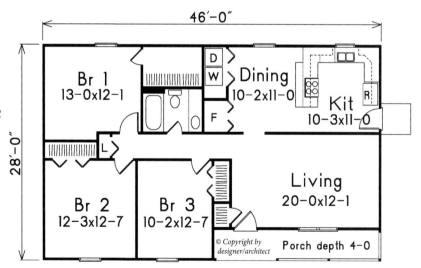

Country Style With Spacious Rooms

- 1,197 total square feet of living area
- U-shaped kitchen includes ample workspace, breakfast bar, laundry area and direct access to the outdoors
- Large living room has a convenient coat closet
- Bedroom #1 features a large walk-in closet
- 2" x 6" exterior walls available, please order plan #539-001D-0102
- 3 bedrooms, 1 bath
- Crawl space foundation, drawings also include basement and slab foundations

46'-0"

28'-0"

Br 1
13-0x12-1

D
W
F

Dining
10-2x11-0

Kit
10-3x11-0

R

L

Br 2
12-3x12-7

Br 3
10-2x12-7

Living
20-0x12-1

© Copyright by designer/architect

Porch depth 4-0

Vaulted Ceilings Show Off This Ranch

- 1,135 total square feet of living area

- Energy efficient home with 2" x 6" exterior walls

- The living room features a vaulted ceiling and a corner fireplace

- The master bedroom offers a vaulted ceiling, private bath and generous closet space

- Compact but functional kitchen is complete with an adjacent utility room

- 3 bedrooms, 2 baths, 2-car garage

- Basement foundation, drawings also include crawl space foundation

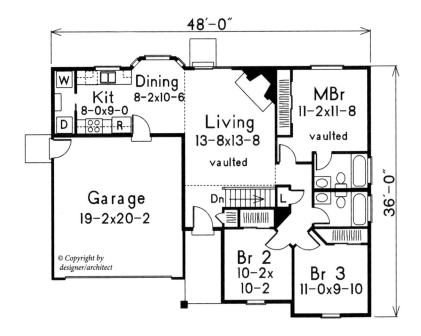

Covered Porch Adds To Perfect Outdoor Getaway

- 733 total square feet of living area
- Bedrooms are separate from the kitchen and living area for privacy
- Lots of closet space throughout this home
- Centrally located bath is easily accessible
- Kitchen features a door accessing the outdoors and a door separating it from the rest of the home
- 2 bedrooms, 1 bath
- Pier foundation

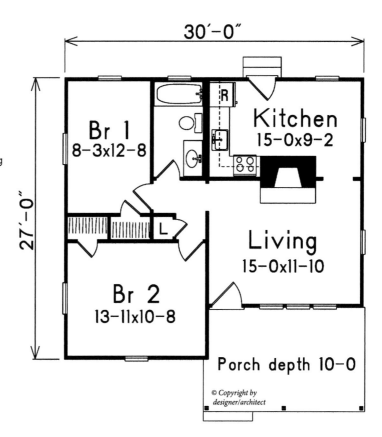

30'-0"

27'-0"

Br 1
8-3x12-8

Kitchen
15-0x9-2

Br 2
13-11x10-8

Living
15-0x11-10

Porch depth 10-0

© Copyright by designer/architect

Easily Converts To A Duplex Home

- 588 total square feet of living area
- May be built as a duplex, 4-car garage or apartment garage/vacation cabin as shown
- Very livable plan in a small footprint
- Living room features a functional entry, bayed dining area, corner fireplace and opens to kitchen with breakfast bar
- 1 bedroom, 1 bath, 2-car side entry garage
- Slab foundation
- 1,176 square feet of living area when built as a duplex

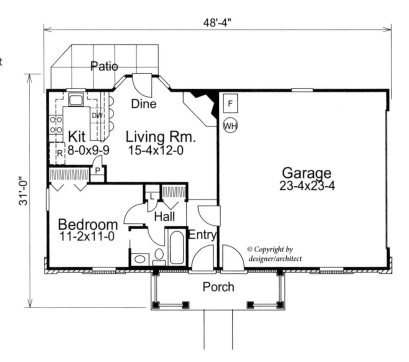

To Order See Page 254 or Call Toll-Free 1-877-379-3420

LOWE'S
LEGACY
SERIES

Classic Ranch With Inviting Covered Front Porch

- 1,317 total square feet of living area
- Galley-style kitchen has convenient access to the basement
- Dining room is joined by the great room creating an open atmosphere
- A well-designed laundry area is nestled between the garage and kitchen
- 3 bedrooms, 2 baths, 2-car garage
- Basement foundation, drawings also include crawl space and slab foundations

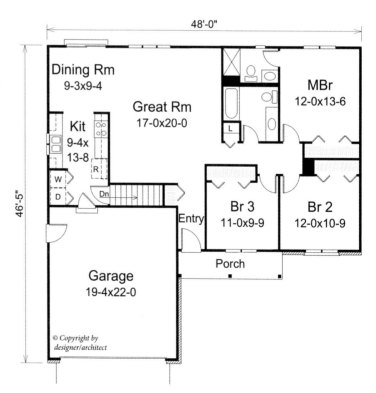

48'-0"

46'-5"

Dining Rm
9-3x9-4

Great Rm
17-0x20-0

Kit
9-4x
13-8

MBr
12-0x13-6

Br 3
11-0x9-9

Br 2
12-0x10-9

Entry

Porch

Garage
19-4x22-0

© Copyright by designer/architect

Flexible Layout For Various Uses

- 1,143 total square feet of living area
- Enormous stone fireplace in the family room adds warmth and character
- Spacious kitchen with breakfast bar overlooks the family room
- Separate dining area is great for entertaining
- Vaulted family room and kitchen create an open atmosphere
- 2" x 6" exterior walls available, please order plan #539-058D-0075
- 2 bedrooms, 1 bath
- Crawl space foundation

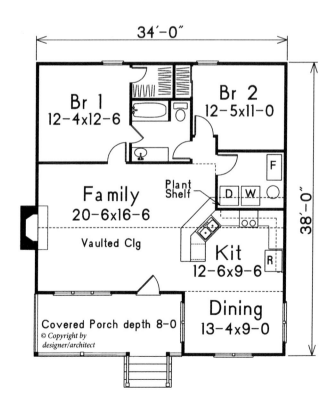

34'-0"

38'-0"

Br 1
12-4x12-6

Br 2
12-5x11-0

F

Plant Shelf

D W

Family
20-6x16-6

Vaulted Clg

Kit
12-6x9-6

R

Covered Porch depth 8-0

© Copyright by designer/architect

Dining
13-4x9-0

Ideal Cottage For Leisure Living

- 496 total square feet of living area
- The traditional front exterior and rear both enjoy shady porches for relaxing evenings
- The living room with bayed dining area is open to a functional L-shaped kitchen with a convenient pantry
- A full bath, large walk-in closet and access to both the rear porch and the garage enhance the spacious bedroom
- 1 bedroom, 1 bath, 2-car garage
- Slab foundation

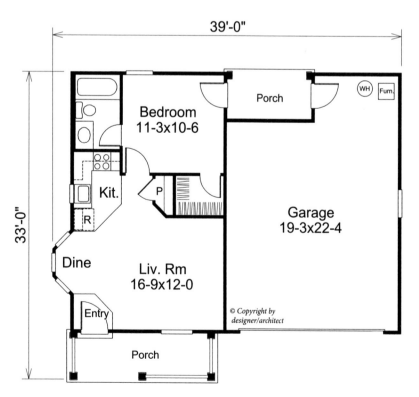

39'-0"

33'-0"

Bedroom
11-3x10-6

Porch

WH   Fur.

Kit.

P

R

Garage
19-3x22-4

Dine

Liv. Rm
16-9x12-0

Entry

© Copyright by designer/architect

Porch

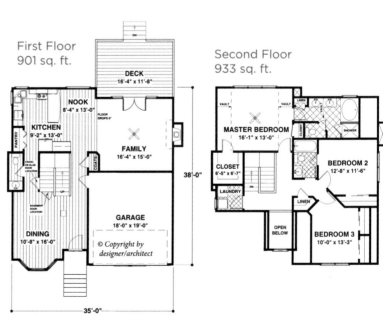

Delightful Chalet

- 1,834 total square feet of living area
- This attractive European-inspired home is designed especially for today's narrow lots and offers a well-planned interior
- Tucked into the back of this home you'll find a family room with double French doors leading onto a deck
- A cozy fireplace can be enjoyed from the family room, breakfast nook and kitchen
- 3 bedrooms, 2 1/2 baths, 2-car garage
- Basement foundation

First Floor
901 sq. ft.

DECK
16'-4" x 11'-8"

NOOK
8'-4" x 13'-0"

FLOOR
DROPS 6"

KITCHEN
9'-2" x 13'-0"

PANTRY

CRAWL
OR SLAB
DOOR
LOCATION

COATS

FAMILY
16'-4" x 15'-0"

BASEMENT
DOOR
LOCATION

UP

38'-0"

GARAGE
18'-0" x 19'-0"

DINING
10'-8" x 16'-0"

© Copyright by
designer/architect

35'-0"

Second Floor
933 sq. ft.

VAULT

VAULT

LINEN

MASTER BEDROOM
16'-1" x 13'-0"

CLOSET

SHOWER

CLOSET
6'-5" x 6'-7"

BEDROOM 2
12'-8" x 11'-6"

LAUNDRY

DN

LINEN

OPEN
BELOW

BEDROOM 3
10'-0" x 13'-3"

Designed For Comfort And Utility

- 720 total square feet of living area
- Abundant windows in the living and kitchen/dining rooms provide generous sunlight
- Secluded laundry area has a handy storage closet nearby
- U-shaped kitchen with large breakfast bar opens into the living room
- Large covered front porch offers plenty of outdoor living space
- 2 bedrooms, 1 bath
- Crawl space foundation, drawings also include slab foundation

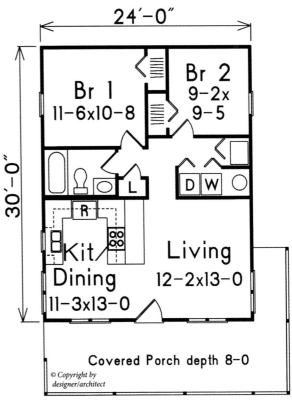

24'-0"

30'-0"

Br 1
11-6x10-8

Br 2
9-2x
9-5

L

D W

R

Kit

Living
12-2x13-0

Dining
11-3x13-0

Covered Porch depth 8-0

© Copyright by designer/architect

Ideal Home Or Retirement Retreat

- 1,013 total square feet of living area
- Vaulted ceilings in both the family room and kitchen
- Plant shelf above the kitchen is a special feature
- Oversized utility room has space for a full-size washer and dryer
- Hall bath is centrally located with easy access from both bedrooms
- 2" x 6" exterior walls available, please order plan #539-058D-0073
- 2 bedrooms, 1 bath
- Slab foundation

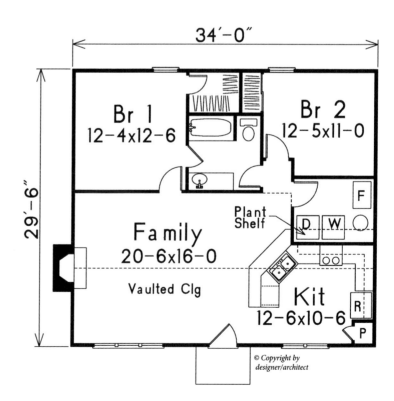

34'-0"

29'-6"

Br 1
12-4x12-6

Br 2
12-5x11-0

Family
20-6x16-0
Vaulted Clg

Plant Shelf

F

D W

Kit
12-6x10-6

R

P

© Copyright by designer/architect

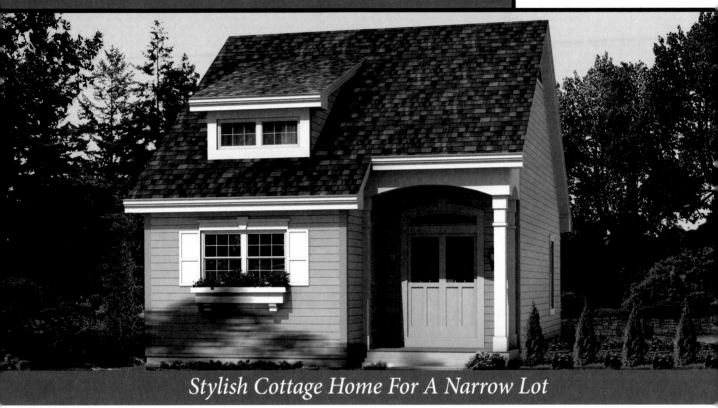

Stylish Cottage Home For A Narrow Lot

- 882 total square feet of living area
- An inviting porch and entry lure you into this warm and cozy home
- Living room features a vaulted ceiling, bayed dining area and is open to a well-equipped U-shaped kitchen
- The master bedroom has two separate closets and direct access to the rear patio
- 2 bedrooms, 1 bath
- Crawl space foundation, drawings also include slab and basement foundations

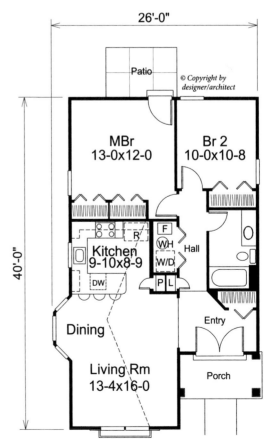

Cottage Style Is Appealing And Cozy

- 828 total square feet of living area
- Vaulted ceiling in living area enhances space
- Convenient laundry room
- Sloped ceiling creates unique style in bedroom #2
- Efficient storage space under the stairs
- Covered entry porch provides a cozy sitting area and plenty of shade
- 2 bedrooms, 1 bath
- Crawl space foundation

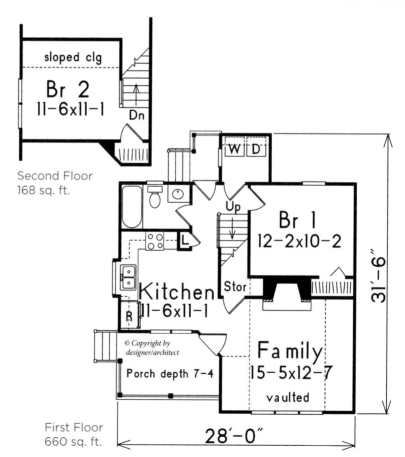

sloped clg

Br 2
11-6x11-1

Dn

Second Floor
168 sq. ft.

W D

Up

Br 1
12-2x10-2

31'-6"

Kitchen
11-6x11-1

Stor

R

© Copyright by
designer/architect

Porch depth 7-4

Family
15-5x12-7

vaulted

First Floor
660 sq. ft.

28'-0"

Cozy And Functional Design

- 1,285 total square feet of living area
- Dining nook has a warm feeling with a sunny box-bay window
- Second floor loft is perfect for a recreation space or office hideaway
- Bedrooms include walk-in closets allowing extra storage space
- Kitchen, dining and living areas combine making a perfect gathering place
- 2 bedrooms, 1 bath
- Crawl space foundation

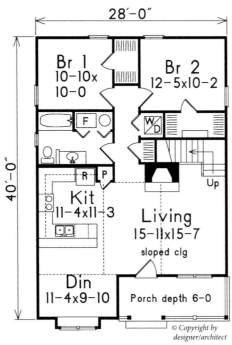

First Floor
1,032 sq. ft.

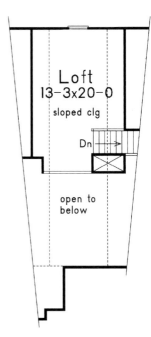

Second Floor
253 sq. ft.

Charming Home With Cozy Porches

- 1,107 total square feet of living area
- L-shaped kitchen has a serving bar overlooking the dining/living room
- Second floor bedrooms share a bath with the linen closet
- Front porch opens into the foyer with convenient coat closet
- 3 bedrooms, 2 baths
- Basement foundation

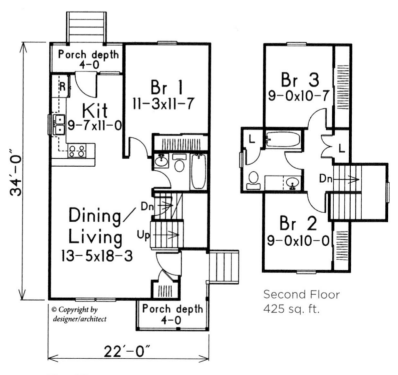

First Floor
682 sq. ft.

Second Floor
425 sq. ft.

© Copyright by designer/architect

Efficient Split-Level Design

- 1,978 total square feet of living area

- Master bedroom includes a walk-in closet and private full bath

- Entry opens into the large living area with bay window, fireplace and plant shelf

- Open kitchen and dining area includes a bar and access to deck

- 4 bedrooms, 3 baths, 2-car drive under side entry garage

- Partial basement/slab foundation, drawings also include basement foundation

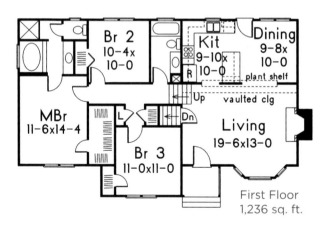

First Floor
1,236 sq. ft.

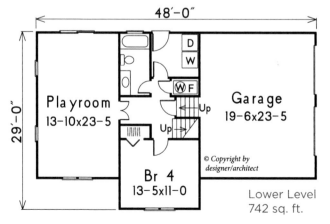

Lower Level
742 sq. ft.

Vacation Retreat With Attractive A-Frame Styling

- 1,312 total square feet of living area
- Expansive deck extends directly off living area
- L-shaped kitchen is organized and efficient
- Bedroom to the left of the kitchen makes a great quiet retreat or office
- Living area is flanked with windows for light
- 3 bedrooms, 1 bath
- Pier foundation

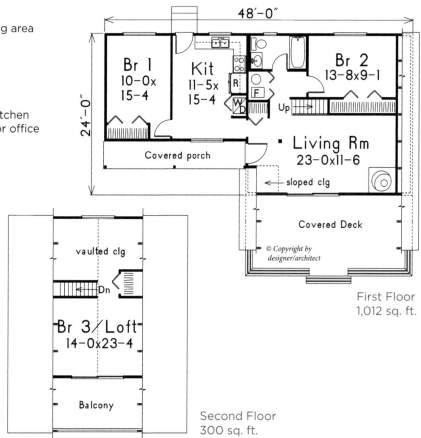

48'-0"

24'-0"

Br 1
10-0x
15-4

Kit
11-5x
15-4

Br 2
13-8x9-1

Covered porch

Up

Living Rm
23-0x11-6

← sloped clg

Covered Deck

© Copyright by
designer/architect

First Floor
1,012 sq. ft.

vaulted clg

Dn

Br 3/Loft
14-0x23-4

Balcony

Second Floor
300 sq. ft.

A Vacation Home For All Seasons

- 1,039 total square feet of living area
- Cathedral construction provides the maximum in living area openness
- Expansive glass viewing walls
- Two decks, front and back
- Charming second story loft arrangement
- Simple, low-maintenance construction
- 2 bedrooms, 1 1/2 baths
- Crawl space foundation

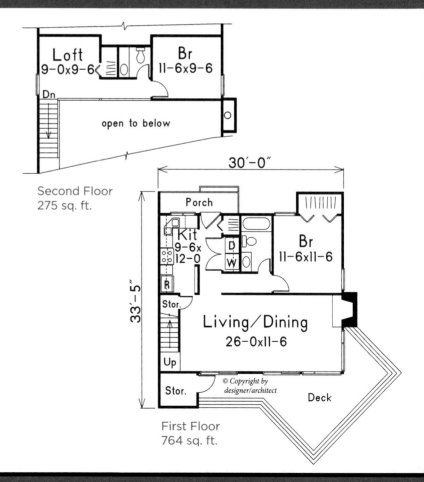

Loft
9-0x9-6

Br
11-6x9-6

Dn

open to below

Second Floor
275 sq. ft.

30'-0"

Porch

Kit
9-6x
12-0

Br
11-6x11-6

33'-5"

D
W

Stor.

Living/Dining
26-0x11-6

Up

Stor.

© Copyright by
designer/architect

Deck

First Floor
764 sq. ft.

Open Layout Ensures Easy Living

- 976 total square feet of living area
- Cozy front porch opens into the large living room
- Convenient half bath is located on the first floor
- All bedrooms are located on the second floor for privacy
- Dining room has access to the outdoors
- 3 bedrooms, 1 1/2 baths
- Basement foundation

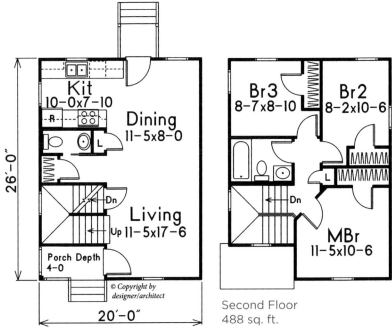

First Floor
488 sq. ft.

Second Floor
488 sq. ft.

© Copyright by
designer/architect

A Chalet For Lakeside Living

- 1,280 total square feet of living area
- Attention to architectural detail has created the look of an authentic Swiss cottage
- Spacious living room, adjacent kitchenette and dining area all enjoy views to the front deck
- Hall bath shared by two sizable bedrooms is included on the first and second floors
- 4 bedrooms, 2 baths
- Crawl space foundation, drawings also include basement foundation

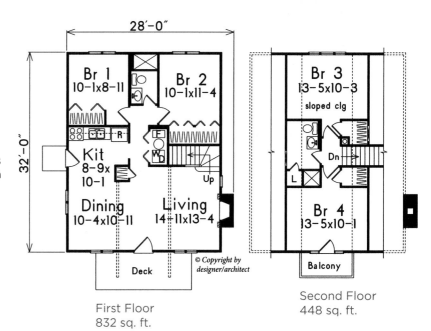

First Floor
832 sq. ft.

Second Floor
448 sq. ft.

Craftsman Style Cottage

- 1,800 total square feet of living area
- Suited for a narrow lot, this bungalow offers tremendous curb appeal and a stylish interior
- An entire wall of windows adds a generous amount of sunlight to the family room
- The master bedroom is separated from the other bedrooms and also enjoys a private bath with shower and whirlpool tub
- 3 bedrooms, 2 baths, 2-car rear entry garage
- Basement foundation

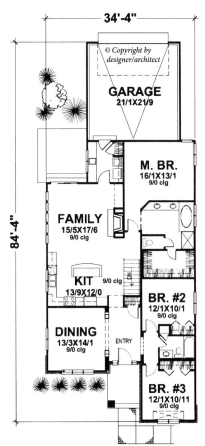

Charming Three-Bedroom Home

- 1,140 total square feet of living area
- Delightful appearance with a protective porch
- The entry, with convenient stairs to the basement, leads to spacious living and dining rooms open to the adjacent kitchen
- The master bedroom enjoys a double-door entry, walk-in closet and a private bath with its own linen closet
- 3 bedrooms, 2 baths, 2-car garage
- Basement foundation, drawings also include slab and crawl space foundations

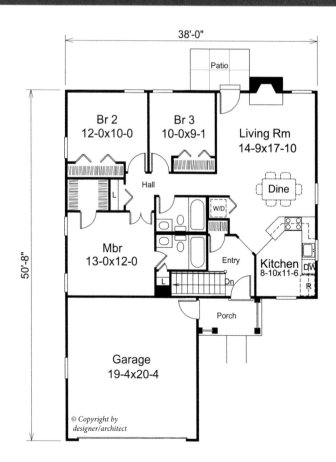

38'-0"

50'-8"

Patio

Br 2
12-0x10-0

Br 3
10-0x9-1

Living Rm
14-9x17-10

Hall

Dine

W/D

Mbr
13-0x12-0

Entry

Kitchen
8-10x11-6

DW

Dn

Porch

Garage
19-4x20-4

© Copyright by
designer/architect

Ideal For A Narrow Lot

- 1,224 total square feet of living area
- The coffered ceiling and corner fireplace provide an impressive entry view
- The adjoining kitchen includes an island with seating that opens to the cozy dining area
- The massive master bedroom features a vaulted ceiling and private bath with double-door entry and walk-in closet
- 3 bedrooms, 2 baths
- Slab foundation

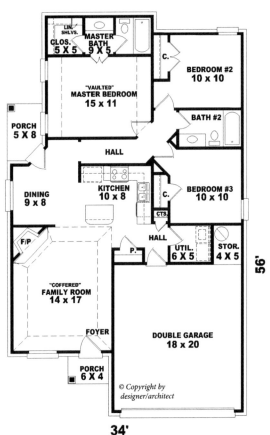

Stately Colonial Features Porch With Overhead Balcony

- 2,216 total square feet of living area
- Luxury master bedroom suite features full-windowed bathtub bay, double walk-in closets and access to the front balcony
- Spacious kitchen has enough space for dining
- Second floor laundry facility is centrally located for convenience
- 4 bedrooms, 2 1/2 baths, 2-car side entry drive under garage
- Basement foundation

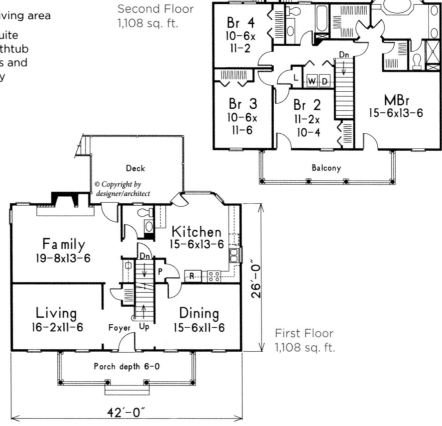

Second Floor
1,108 sq. ft.

First Floor
1,108 sq. ft.

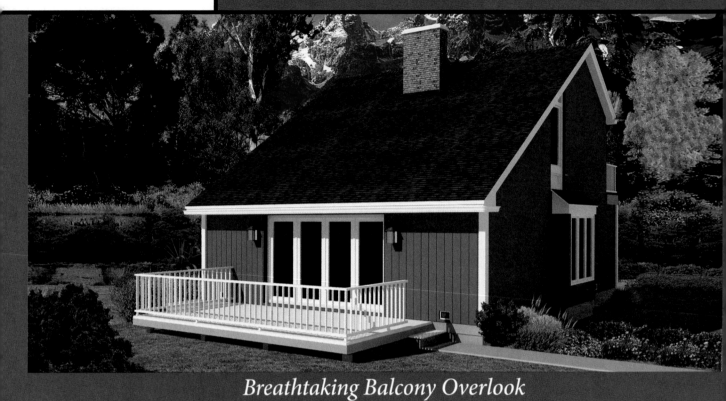

Breathtaking Balcony Overlook

- 1,299 total square feet of living area
- Convenient storage for skis, etc. is located outside the front entrance
- The kitchen and dining room receive light from the box-bay window
- Large vaulted living room features a cozy fireplace and overlook from the second floor balcony
- Two second floor bedrooms share a Jack and Jill bath
- Second floor balcony extends over the entire length of the living room below
- 3 bedrooms, 2 baths
- Crawl space foundation, drawings also include slab foundation

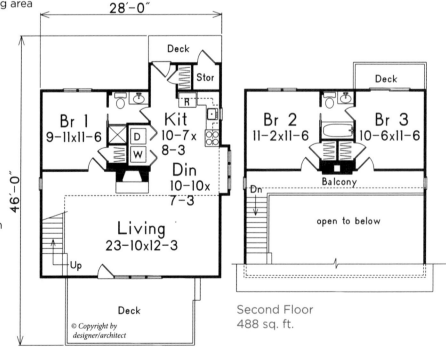

First Floor
811 sq. ft.

Second Floor
488 sq. ft.

Quaint Cottage With Inviting Front Porch

- 1,020 total square feet of living area
- Living room is warmed by a fireplace
- Dining and living rooms are enhanced by vaulted ceilings and plant shelves
- U-shaped kitchen features a large window over the sink
- 2 bedrooms, 1 bath
- Slab foundation

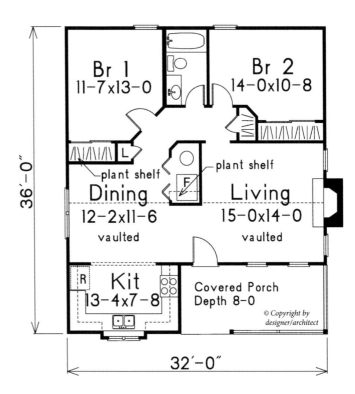

Cheerful Narrow Lot Home

- 2,296 total square feet of living area

- The highly functional kitchen offers double snack bars, a pantry and an adjacent breakfast nook

- Located off of the breakfast nook is an oversized laundry room with plenty of space for a washer and dryer as well as a laundry sink and upright freezer

- The spacious master bedroom, with its bowed window, tray ceiling, sitting area, luxurious bath and abundant closet, is truly an owner's retreat

- The second floor features two secondary bedroom suites, each featuring a walk-in closet and private bath

- 3 bedrooms, 3 1/2 baths, 2-car garage

- Crawl space foundation

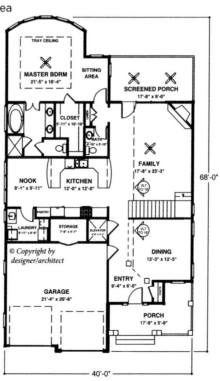

First Floor
1,636 sq. ft.

Second Floor
660 sq. ft.

FREE *Lowe's Gift Card Offer*

Lowe's Special Rebate Offer

Purchase any plan package featured in this book PLUS at least $15,000 of your materials from Lowe's and receive a gift card for the purchase price of your plans.

To receive the rebate:

1. Purchase any of the plan packages in this publication PLUS at least $15,000 of the materials to build your home at Lowe's before 12/31/13. Requests must be postmarked by 1/31/14. Claims postmarked after this date will not be honored.

2. Limit one gift card per set of plans.

3. Please allow 3-4 weeks for processing. If you do not receive a gift card after 4 weeks, visit www.lowes.com/rebates, or you may call 1-877-204-1223.

4. Please keep a copy of all materials submitted for your records.

5. Copy the entire sale receipt(s), including store name, location, purchase date, and invoice number, showing blueprint purchase and total amount spent.

6. Mail this complete page with your name, address and other information below, along with a copy of the receipt(s).

Name_____

Street Address _____

City _____

State/Zip_____

Daytime phone number (____) - _____

E-mail address _____

Plan number purchased 539-_____

I purchased a ☐ One-Set Plan Package
                ☐ Five-Set Plan Package
                ☐ Eight-Set Plan Package
                ☐ Reproducible Masters
                ☐ Builder's CAD Package

MAIL TO:

Lowe's Free Gift Card Offer
P.O. Box 3029
Young America, MN 55558-3029

Check the status of your rebate at www.lowes.com/rebates

Other terms and conditions. Requests from groups will not be honored. Fraudulent submission of multiple requests could result in federal prosecution under the U.S. Mail Fraud Statutes (18 USC, Section 1341 and 1342). Offer good in the U.S.A. only. Void where prohibited, taxed or restricted by law. If you do not receive your rebate within 3-4 weeks, please call 1-877-204-1223 or visit www.lowes.com/rebates. This page may not be reproduced, traded or sold. Please keep a copy for future reference.

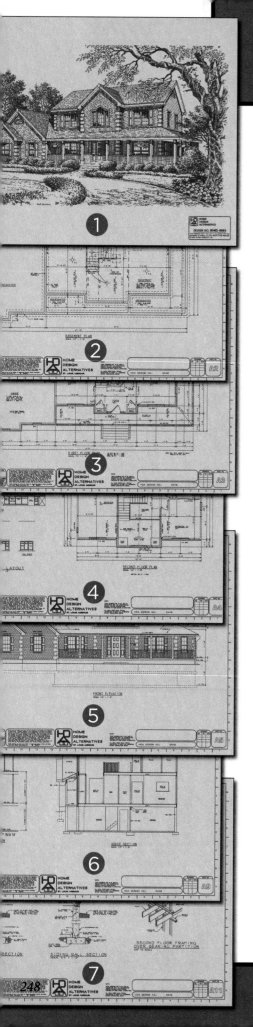

Our Blueprint Packages Include...

**Quality plans for building your future,
with extras that provide unsurpassed value,
ensure good construction and long-term enjoyment.**

A quality home - one that looks good, functions well, and provides years of enjoyment - is a product of many things - design, materials, and craftsmanship.

But it's also the result of outstanding blueprints - the actual plans and specifications that tell the builder exactly how to build your home.

And with our BLUEPRINT PACKAGES you get the absolute best. A complete set of blueprints is available for every design in this book. These "working drawings" are highly detailed, resulting in two key benefits:

- Better understanding by the contractor of how to build your home and...

- More accurate construction estimates.

1. Cover Sheet is the artist's rendering of the exterior of the home and is included with many of the plans. It will give you an idea of how your home will look when completed and landscaped.

2. Foundation plan shows the layout of the basement, crawl space, slab or pier foundation. All necessary notations and dimensions are included. See the plan page for the foundation types included. If the home plan you choose does not have your desired foundation type, our Customer Service Representatives can advise you on how to customize your foundation to suit your specific needs or site conditions.

3. Floor Plans show the placement of walls, doors, closets, plumbing fixtures, electrical outlets, columns, and beams for each level of the home.

4. Interior Elevations provide views of special interior elements such as fireplaces, kitchen cabinets, built-in units and other features of the home.

5. Exterior Elevations illustrate the front, rear and both sides of the house, with all details of exterior materials and the required dimensions.

6. Sections show detail views of the home or portions of the home as if it were sliced from the roof to the foundation. This sheet shows important areas such as load-bearing walls, stairs, joists, trusses and other structural elements, which are critical for proper construction.

7. Details show how to construct certain components of your home, such as the roof system, stairs, deck, etc.

What Kind Of Plan Package Do You Need?

Now that you've found the home you've been looking for, here are some suggestions on how to make your Dream Home a reality. To get started, order the type of plans that fit your particular situation.

Your Choices

☐ *The One-Set Study Package* - We offer a One-set plan package so you can study your home in detail. This one set is considered a study set and is marked "not for construction." It is a copyright violation to reproduce blueprints.

☐ *The Minimum 5-Set Package* - If you're ready to start the construction process, this 5-set package is the minimum number of blueprint sets you will need. It will require keeping close track of each set so they can be used by multiple subcontractors and tradespeople.

☐ *The Standard 8-Set Package* - For best results in terms of cost, schedule and quality of construction, we recommend you order eight (or more) sets of blueprints. Besides one set for yourself, additional sets of blueprints will be required by your mortgage lender, local building department, general contractor and all subcontractors working on foundation, electrical, plumbing, heating/air conditioning, carpentry work, etc.

☐ *Reproducible Masters* - If you wish to make some minor design changes, you'll want to order reproducible masters. These drawings contain the same information as the blueprints but are printed on reproducible paper and clearly indicates your right to alter, copy or reproduce. This will allow your builder or a local design professional to make the necessary drawing changes without the major expense of redrawing the plans. This package also allows you to print copies of the modified plans as needed. The right of building only one structure from these plans is licensed exclusively to the buyer. You may not use this design to build a second or multiple dwelling(s) without purchasing another blueprint. Each violation of the Copyright Law is punishable in a fine.

☐ *Mirror Reverse Sets* - Plans can be printed in mirror reverse. These plans are useful when the house would fit your site better if all the rooms were on the opposite side than shown. They are simply a mirror image of the original drawings causing the lettering and dimensions to read backwards. Therefore, when ordering mirror reverse drawings, you must purchase at least one set of right-reading plans. Some of our plans are offered mirror reverse right-reading. This means the plan, lettering and dimensions are flipped but read correctly. See the Home Plan Index on page 251-252 for availability.

☐ *PDF File Format* - A complete set of construction drawings in an electronic format that allows you to resize and reproduce the plans to fit your needs. Since these are electronic files, we can send them to you within 24 hours (Mon-Fri, 8-5 CST) via email and save you shipping costs. They also offer printing flexibility by allowing you to print the size and number of sets you need.

Note: These are not CAD files and cannot be altered electronically.

☐ *CAD Packages* - A CAD package is a complete set of construction drawings in an electronic file format. They are especially beneficial if you have a significant amount of changes to make to the home plan you have selected or if you need to make the home plan fit your local codes. If you purchase a CAD Package, you have the option to take the plan to a local design professional who uses AutoCAD or DataCAD and they can modify the design much easier and quicker than with a paper-based drawing, which will help save you time and money. Just like our reproducible masters, with a CAD package you will receive a one-time build copyright release that allows you to make changes and the necessary copies needed to build your home. For more information and availability, please call our Customer Service Department at 1-877-379-3420.

Your Blueprint Package will contain the necessary construction information to build your home. We also offer the following products and services to save you time and money in the building process.

Material List

Material lists are available for all of the plans in this book. Each list gives you the quantity, dimensions and description of the building materials necessary to construct your home. You'll get faster and more accurate bids from your contractor while saving money by paying for only the materials you need. See your Commercial Sales Specialist at your local Lowe's Store to receive a free take-off.

Note: The material list is designed with the standard foundation only and does not include alternate or optional foundations.

Express Delivery

Most orders are processed within 24 hours of receipt. Please allow 7-10 business days for delivery. If you need to place a rush order, please call us by 11:00 a.m. Monday through Friday, 8am-5pm CST and ask for express service (allow 1-2 business days).

Technical Assistance

If you have questions, call our technical support line at 1-314-770-2228 Monday through Friday, 8am-5pm CST. Whether it involves design modifications or field assistance, our designers are extremely familiar with all of our designs and will be happy to help you. We want your home to be everything you expect it to be.

Other Great Products...

Below are a few products sure to help the beginner as well as the experienced builder.

Legal Kit

Home building can be a complicated process with many legal regulations being confusing. This Legal Kit was designed to help you avoid many legal pitfalls and build your home with confidence using the forms and contracts featured in this kit. Included are request for proposal documents, various fixed price and cost plus contracts, instructions on how and when to use each form, warranty statements and more. Save time and money before you break ground on your new home or start a remodeling project. Instructions are included on how to use the kit and since the documents are universal, they are designed to be used with all building trades. Since review by an attorney is always advised before signing any contract, this is an ideal way to get organized and started on the process. Plus, all forms are reproducible making it a terrific tool for the contractor and home builder. At a price of $35.00, this kit is ideal.

Detail Plan Packages
Framing, Plumbing and Electrical Plan Packages

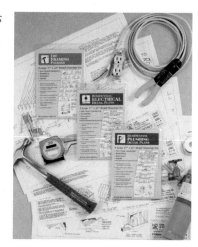

Three separate packages offer home builders details for constructing various foundations; numerous floor, wall and roof framing techniques; simple to complex residential wiring; sump and water softener hookups; plumbing connection methods; installation of septic systems, and more. Packages include 3-dimensional illustrations and a glossary of terms. These drawings do not pertain to a specific home plan making them perfect for your building situation.

Each package is $20 or purchase all three for $40 making it a great bargain.

To order any of the products on this page, please see the Home Plan order form on page 254.

Home Plan Index

Before You Order

Exchange Policies

Since blueprints are printed in response to your order, we cannot honor requests for refunds. However, if for some reason you find that the plan you have purchased does not meet your requirements, you may exchange that plan for another plan in our collection within 90 days of purchase. At the time of the exchange, you will be charged a processing fee of 25% of your original plan package price, plus the difference in price between the plan packages (if applicable) and the cost to ship the new plans to you.

Please note: Reproducible drawings can only be exchanged if the package is unopened. PDF and CAD files are not returnable and non-refundable.

Building Codes & Requirements

At the time the construction drawings were prepared, every effort was made to ensure that these plans and specifications meet nationally recognized codes. Our plans conform to most national building codes. Because building codes vary from area to area, some drawing modifications and/or the assistance of a professional designer or architect may be necessary to comply with your local codes or to accommodate specific building site conditions. We advise you to consult with your local building official for information regarding codes governing your area.

Additional Sets†

Additional sets of the plan ordered are available for an additional cost of $45.00 each. Five-set, eight-set, and reproducible packages offer considerable savings.

† Available only within 90 days after purchase of plan package or reproducible masters of the same plan.

Blueprint Price Schedule

BEST VALUE

Price Code	1-Set	SAVE $80 5-Sets	SAVE $115 8 Sets	PDF File/ Reproducible Masters
AAA	$310	$410	$510	$610
AA	$410	$510	$610	$710
A	$470	$570	$670	$770
B	$530	$630	$730	$830
C	$585	$685	$785	$885
D	$635	$735	$835	$935
E	$695	$795	$895	$995
F	$750	$850	$950	$1,050
G	$1,000	$1,100	$1,200	$1,300
H	$1,100	$1,200	$1,300	$1,400
I	$1,150	$1,250	$1,350	$1,450
J	$1,200	$1,300	$1,400	$1,500
K	$1,250	$1,350	$1,450	$1,550

Plan prices are subject to change without notice.
Please note that plans and material lists are not refundable.

Shipping & Handling Charges

U.S. Shipping - (AK & HI express only)	1-4 Sets	5-7 Sets	8 Sets or Reproducibles
Regular (allow 7-10 business days)	$15.00	$17.50	$25.00
Priority (allow 3-5 business days)	$35.00	$40.00	$45.00
Express* (allow 1-2 business days)	$50.00	$55.00	$60.00

Canada Shipping (to/from)**			
Standard (allow 8-12 business days)	$35.00	$40.00	$45.00
Express* (allow 3-5 business days)	$75.00	$85.00	$95.00

Overseas Shipping/International -

Call, fax, or e-mail (plans@hdainc.com) for shipping costs.
 * For express delivery please call us by 11:00 a.m. Monday-Friday CST
** Orders may be subject to custom's fee and/or duties/taxes.

NOTE: Shipping and handling charges do not apply on PDF files.
Orders will be emailed within 24 hours (Mon-Fri., 8-5 CST) of purchase.

Questions? Call Our Customer Service Number
1-877-379-3420

Many of our plans are available in CAD.
For availability, please call our Customer Service Number above.

Order Form

1.) *Call* toll-free 1-877-379-3420 for credit card orders. Mastercard, Visa, Discover and American Express are accepted.

2.) *Fax* your order to 1-314-770-2226.

3.) *Mail* the Order Form to: HDA, Inc.
944 Anglum Road
St. Louis, MO 63042
attn: Customer Service Dept.

4.) *Visit* your Commercial Sales Specialist at your local Lowe's store.

For fastest service, Call Toll-Free
1-877-379-3420 day or night

Order Form

Please send me -

PLAN NUMBER 539-_____

PRICE CODE_____ *(see pages 251-252)*

Specify Foundation Type *(see plan page for availability)*

☐ Slab ☐ Crawl space ☐ Pier

☐ Basement ☐ Walk-out basement

☐ Reproducible Masters $_____

☐ PDF File $_____

☐ Eight-Set Plan Package $_____

☐ Five-Set Plan Package $_____

☐ One-Set Study Package *(no mirror reverse)* $_____

☐ CAD Package *(call for availability)* $_____

Additional Plan Sets† *(see page 252)*

☐ ____ (Qty.) at $45.00 each $_____

Mirror Reverse† *(see page 249)*

☐ Right-reading $150 one-time charge
(see index on pages 251-252 for availability) $_____

☐ Print in Mirror Reverse
(where right-reading is not available)

____ (Qty.) at $15.00 each $_____

☐ Legal Kit *(002D-9991, see page 250)* $_____

Detail Plan Packages: *(see page 250)*

☐ Framing ☐ Electrical ☐ Plumbing $_____
(002D-9992)   (002D-9993)   (002D-9994)

SUBTOTAL $_____

Sales Tax *(MO residents add 7%)* $_____

☐ Shipping / Handling *(see page 253)* $_____

TOTAL *(US funds only - sorry no CODs)* $_____

I hereby authorize HDA, Inc. to charge this purchase to my credit card account (check one):

☐ MasterCard ☐ VISA ☐ DISCOVER ☐ AMERICAN EXPRESS Cards

Plan prices are subject to change without notice.
Please note that plans and material lists are not refundable.

Credit Card number _____

Expiration date _____

Signature _____

Name_____
(Please print or type)

Street Address_____
(Please do not use a PO Box)

_____

City _____

State _____

Zip _____

Daytime phone number (_____) - _____

E-mail address _____

I am a ☐ Builder/Contractor

☐ Homeowner

☐ Renter

I ☐ have ☐ have not selected my general contractor.

Thank you for your order!

†Available only within 90 days after purchase of plan package or reproducible masters of same plan.
Note: Shipping and handling does not apply for PDF files. Orders will be emailed within 24 hours (Mon.-Fri., 8am-5pm CST) of purchase.

The Lowe's Legacy Series
Apartment Garages

HDA, Inc. is proud to introduce to you the Lowe's Legacy Series. The apartment garages in this collection carry on the Lowe's tradition of quality and expertise, and will continue to do so for many generations.

Choosing an apartment garage can be a bit overwhelming. With the Legacy Series, we will set your mind at ease. Selecting a plan from this group will ensure a plan designed with the Lowe's standard of excellence.

This collection of Legacy Series plans includes our most popular apartment garage plans. Browse through the pages to discover an apartment garage with the options and special characteristics you need.

Along with one-of-a-kind craftsmanship, all Legacy Series plans offer industry-leading material lists. These accurate material lists will save you a considerable amount of time and money, providing you with the quantity, dimensions and descriptions of the major building materials necessary to construct your apartment garage. You'll get faster and more accurate bids from your contractor while saving money by paying for only the materials you need.

The Lowe's Legacy Series is the place to start your search for the perfect plan. You will find the expected beauty you want and the functional efficiency you need, all designed with unmatched quality.

Turn the page and begin the wonderful journey of finding the perfect apartment garage.

Photos clockwise from top: 539-009D-7508, page 280; 539-009D-7514, page 279; 539-009D-7513, page 259; 539-013L-0163, page 258.

Delightful Two-Car Garage Apartment

- 792 square feet
- Roof pitch - 8/12
- Ceiling heights:
  First floor - 9'
  Second floor - 8'
- 1 bedroom, 1 bath
- Two 9' x 8' overhead doors
- The living area is entirely open and consists of the kitchen, eating space and family room
- An abundance of storage space is offered, including a walk-in pantry and two closets in the bedroom
- The covered porch offers an enchanting atmosphere for enjoying the outdoors

Second Floor

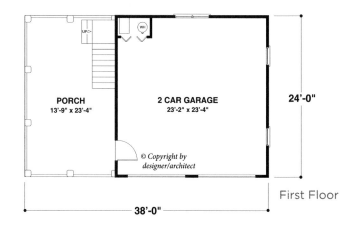

First Floor

Lovely Brick Exterior

- 1,240 square feet
- Building height - 27'
- Roof pitch - 6/12, 9/12, 12/12
- Ceiling heights:
  First floor - 9'
  Second floor - 8'
- 2 bedrooms, 1 bath
- Two 9' x 8' overhead doors
- Kitchen/breakfast area combine for added spaciousness
- Sloped ceiling adds appeal in sitting area
- Complete list of materials

Second Floor

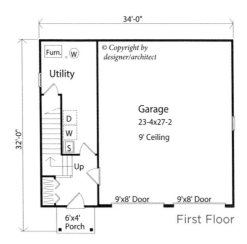

First Floor

Plan #539-013L-0163 • Price Code B

Arts And Crafts Three-Car Garage Apartment

- 838 square feet
- Building height - 23'-9"
- Roof pitch - 12/12
- Ceiling heights:
  First floor - 8'
  Second floor - 9'
- 1 bedroom, 1 bath
- Three 9' x 8' overhead doors
- Stone columns and a planter box decorate the exterior of this lovely apartment home
- Inside, the garage conveniently houses a washer/dryer unit
- An abundance of storage can be found throughout the unit, including built-in shelves in the family room and a pantry in the kitchen
- Lots of closet space

Second Floor

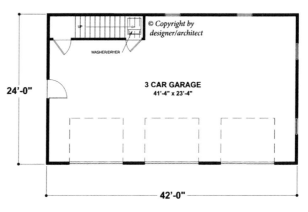

First Floor

Cozy 2-Car Garage Apartment

- 615 square feet
- Building height - 25'-4"
- Roof pitch - 8/12, 10/12
- Ceiling heights:
  First floor - 8'
  Second floor - 8'
- 1 bedroom, 1 bath
- 16' x 7' overhead door
- Living room enjoys a fireplace with shelving and is open to the kitchen with an eating area
- Lots of closet space
- Complete list of materials

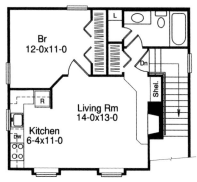

Second Floor

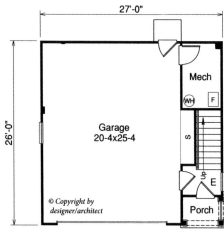

First Floor

Apartment Garage With Pizzazz

- 1,086 square feet
- Building height - 21'-6"
- Roof pitch - 3/12, 5/12
- Ceiling heights:
  First floor - 8'
  Second floor - 8'
- 1 bedroom, 1 1/2 baths
- Two 9' x 7' overhead doors
- Slab foundation
- Open to the living room, the U-shaped kitchen has a snack bar and adjacent laundry area with large storage pantry
- Double doors, clerestory roof and a columned porch all add a sense of charm and class
- Complete list of materials
- Step-by-step instructions

Second Floor
495 sq. ft.

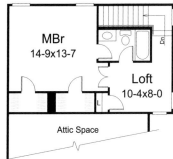

First Floor
591 sq. ft.

3-Car Garage With Rear Apartment

- 1,005 square feet

- Building height - 25'

- Roof pitch - 3.5/12, 6/12, 8/12

- Ceiling heights:
  First floor - 9'
  Second floor - 8'

- 2 bedrooms, 1 1/2 baths

- Three 9' x 8' overhead doors

- Two-story apartment is disguised with one-story facade featuring triple garage doors and roof dormer

- Complete list of materials

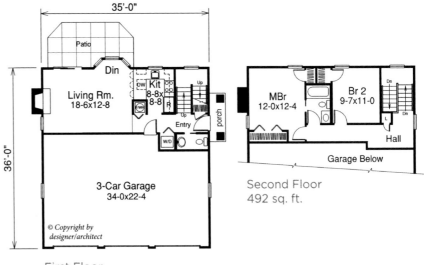

First Floor
513 sq. ft.

Second Floor
492 sq. ft.

Gambrel Roof And Decorative Shutters

- 604 square feet
- Building height - 21'-4"
- Roof pitch - 4/12, 12/4.75
- Ceiling heights:
  First floor - 8'
  Second floor - 8'
- 1 studio area, 1 bath
- Two 9' x 7' overhead doors
- Charming Dutch-Colonial style
- Spacious studio provides extra storage space
- Complete list of materials
- Step-by-step instructions

Second Floor

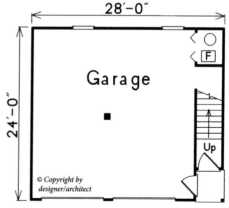

First Floor

3-Car Garage Apartment With Two Entrances

- 949 square feet
- Building height - 24'-10"
- Roof pitch - 6/12
- Ceiling heights:
  First floor - 9'
  Second floor - 8'
- 1 bedroom, 1 bath
- Three 9' x 7' overhead doors
- Sitting area includes an attractive window seat which becomes the focal point
- Complete list of materials

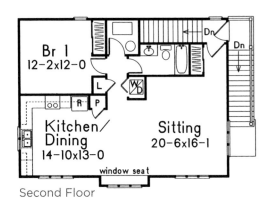

Second Floor

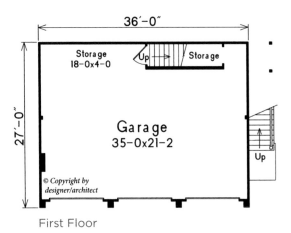

First Floor

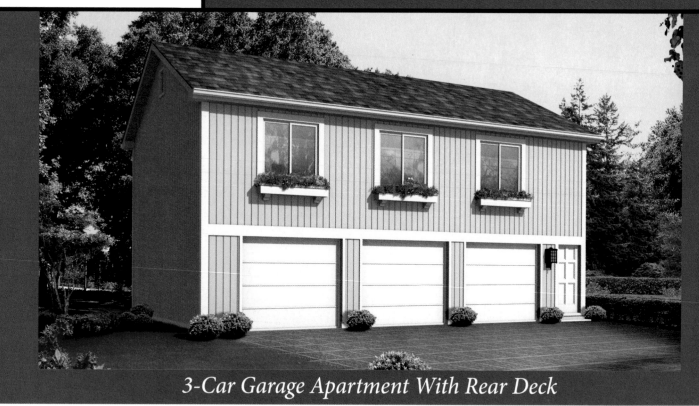

3-Car Garage Apartment With Rear Deck

- 1,040 square feet
- Building height - 23'
- Roof pitch - 5/12
- Ceiling heights:
  First floor - 8'
  Second floor - 8'
- 2 bedrooms, 1 bath
- Three 9' x 7' overhead doors
- Large rooms offer comfortable living with second floor laundry, ample cabinets and sliding doors to deck
- Complete list of materials

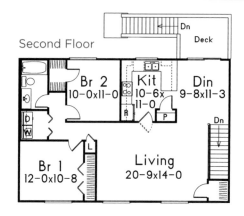

Second Floor

Dn

Deck

Br 2
10-0x11-0

Kit
10-6x
11-0

Din
9-8x11-3

Dn

Br 1
12-0x10-8

Living
20-9x14-0

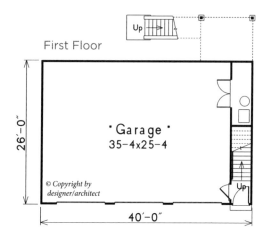

First Floor

Up

Garage
35-4x25-4

Dn

© Copyright by designer/architect

26'-0"

40'-0"

Up

To Order See Page 288 or Call Toll-Free 1-877-379-3420

Lovely Cottage Retreat

- 641 square feet
- Building height - 21'
- Roof pitch - 6/12
- Ceiling heights:
  First floor - 8'
  Second floor - 8'
- 1 bedroom, 1 1/2 baths
- 9' x 7' overhead door
- Charming exterior enjoys a wrap-around porch and a large feature window with arch and planter box
- Complete list of materials

28'-0"

31'-0"

Garage
21-4x11-8

© Copyright by
designer/architect

Stor.

Living Rm.
14-6x14-2

UP
Entry

Porch

First Floor
330 sq. ft.

Bedroom
15-10x11-8

Plant shelf below

DN

Second Floor
311 sq. ft.

Brightening Box-Bay Breakfast Area

- 973 square feet
- Building height - 24'-8"
- Roof pitch - 6/12
- Ceiling heights:
  First floor - 8'
  Second floor - 8'
- 2 bedrooms, 1 bath
- 9' x 7', 16' x 7' overhead doors
- Sunny breakfast room is positioned between the kitchen and the family room for convenience
- Complete list of materials

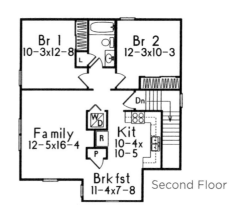

Br 1
10-3x12-8

Br 2
12-3x10-3

Family
12-5x16-4

Kit
10-4x 10-5

Brkfst
11-4x7-8

Second Floor

31'-4"

Storage
7-4x12-4

Garage
31-0x22-11

32'-0"

© Copyright by designer/architect

First Floor

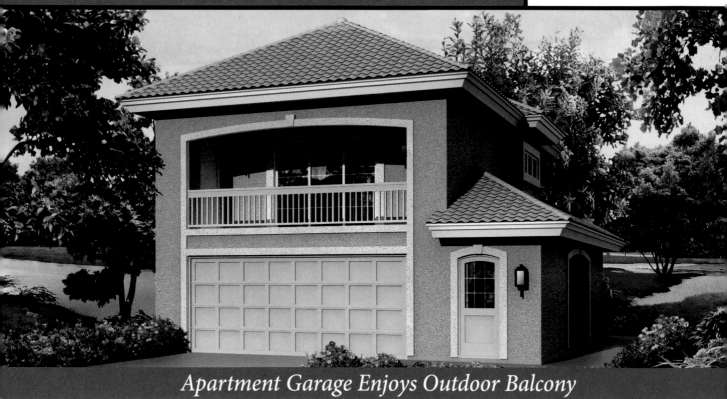

Apartment Garage Enjoys Outdoor Balcony

- 1,091 square feet
- Building height - 25'-6"
- Roof pitch - 6/12
- Ceiling heights:
  First floor - 8'
  Second floor - 8'
- 1 bedroom, 1 bath
- 18' x 7' overhead door
- Slab foundation
- A large side covered porch invites you into the entry hall featuring a coat closet, room for an office or shop, a mechanical room and stairs to the living area above
- The second floor living room, with 9' sliding door to the covered outdoor balcony is open to a U-shaped kitchen with dining bay, built-in pantry and snack counter
- A roomy compartmented bath with walk-in closet adjoins the bedroom that features double entry doors
- Complete list of materials

First Floor
357 sq. ft.

Second Floor
734 sq. ft.

2-Car Garage Apartment With Fireplace

- 628 square feet
- Building height - 26'-6"
- Roof pitch - 8/12, 9/12
- Ceiling heights:
  First floor - 9'
  Second floor - 8'
- 1 bedroom, 1 bath
- 16' x 7' overhead door
- Cozy living room offers vaulted ceiling, fireplace and a pass-through kitchen
- Complete list of materials

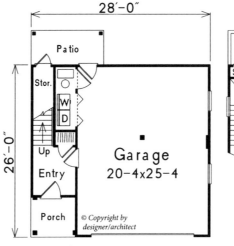

28'-0"

26'-0"

Patio

Stor.

W
D

Up

Entry

Porch

Garage
20-4x25-4

© Copyright by designer/architect

First Floor

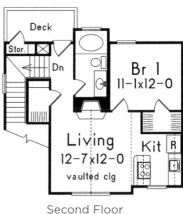

Deck

Stor.

Dn

Br 1
11-1x12-0

Living
12-7x12-0
vaulted clg

Kit
R

Second Floor

Open And Airy Family Room

- 1,032 square feet
- Building height - 24'
- Roof pitch - 5/12, 10/12
- Ceiling heights:
  First floor - 8'
  Second floor - 8'
- 2 bedrooms, 1 bath
- Three 9' x 7' overhead doors
- Spacious family room flows into kitchen/breakfast area
- Two sunny bedrooms share a bath
- Complete list of materials

Second Floor

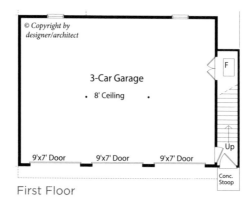

First Floor

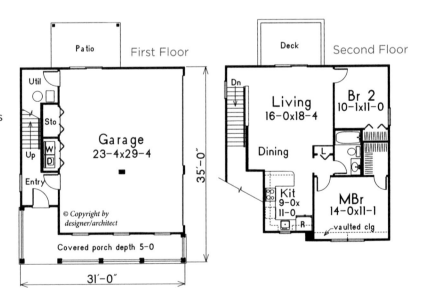

Plan #539-009D-7504 • Price Code P13

Country Garage Apartment With Covered Front Porch

- 929 square feet
- Building height - 27'
- Roof pitch - 6.5/12, 10/12
- Ceiling heights:
  First floor - 9'
  Second floor - 8'
- 2 bedrooms, 1 bath,
  3-car side entry garage
- 16' x 8' and 9' x 8' overhead doors
- Spacious living room with dining area has access to 8' x 12' deck
- Complete list of materials

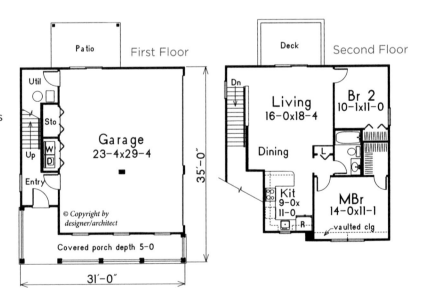

First Floor

Patio

Util

Sto

Up

W/D

Entry

Garage
23-4x29-4

© Copyright by
designer/architect

Covered porch depth 5-0

35'-0"

31'-0"

Second Floor

Deck

Dn

Living
16-0x18-4

Dining

Br 2
10-1x11-0

Kit
9-0x
11-0

MBr
14-0x11-1

vaulted clg

Dormers Add Character To This Apartment Garage

- 568 square feet
- Building height - 26'
- Roof pitch - 12/12
- Ceiling heights:
  First floor - 9'
  Second floor - 8'
- 1 bedroom/sleeping area, 1 bath
- Two 9' x 8' overhead doors
- Beautiful dormers brighten interior
- Complete list of materials

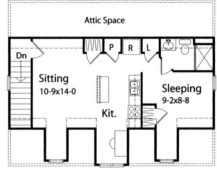

Attic Space

Dn

Sitting
10-9x14-0

Kit.

P R L

Sleeping
9-2x8-8

Second Floor

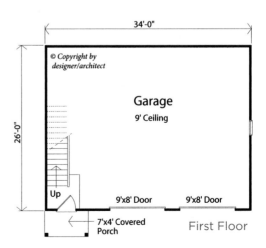

34'-0"

© Copyright by
designer/architect

26'-0"

Garage
9' Ceiling

Up

9'x8' Door   9'x8' Door

7'x4' Covered
Porch

First Floor

Apartment Garage Plus RV Storage

- 713 square feet
- Building height - 25'
- Roof pitch - 6.5/12, 3.5/12
- Ceiling heights:
  First floor - 9'
  Second floor - 8'
  RV garage - 13'-4"
- 1 bedroom, 1 1/2 baths
- 18' x 8' & 12' x 12' overhead doors
- Complete list of materials

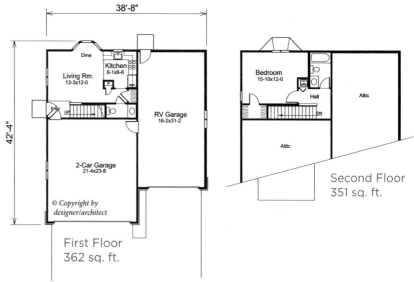

First Floor
362 sq. ft.

Second Floor
351 sq. ft.

Charming Garage Apartment

- 701 square feet

- Building height - 26'

- Roof pitch - 6/12, 8/12, 9/12

- Ceiling heights:
  First floor - 9'
  Second floor - 8'

- 1 bedroom, 1 bath

- Two 9' x 7' overhead doors

- Open living areas
  add spaciousness

- Complete list of materials

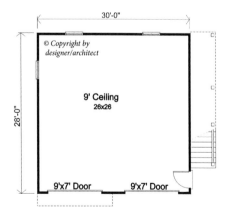

First Floor

30'-0"

© Copyright by
designer/architect

9' Ceiling
26x26

28'-0"

9'x7' Door   9'x7' Door

Second Floor

Kitchen
8-4x7

Dining
13x10-4

MBr.
12x10-9

Great Room
13x11

Stylish Apartment Garage With Covered Front Porch

- 1,026 square feet
- Building height - 25'
- Roof pitch - 8/12
- Ceiling heights:
  First floor - 9'
  Second floor - 8'
- 1 bedroom, 1 1/2 baths
- Two 16' x 7' overhead doors
- A one-story look, clerestory roof dormer and nice symmetry all help to create this handsome exterior
- Complete list of materials

Second Floor
439 sq. ft.

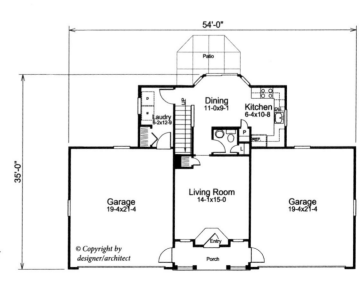

First Floor
587 sq. ft.

Triple Dormers Grace Exterior

- 1,240 square feet
- Building height - 27'
- Roof pitch - 6/12, 9/12, 12/12
- Ceiling heights:
  First floor - 9'
  Second floor - 8'
- 1 bedroom, 1 bath
- Two 9' x 8' overhead doors
- Kitchen/breakfast area includes island ideal for food preparation or dining
- Spacious bath directly accesses the bedroom as well as the sitting area
- Complete list of materials

Second Floor

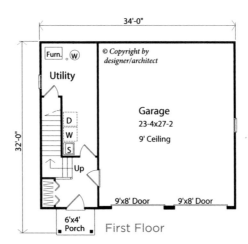

First Floor

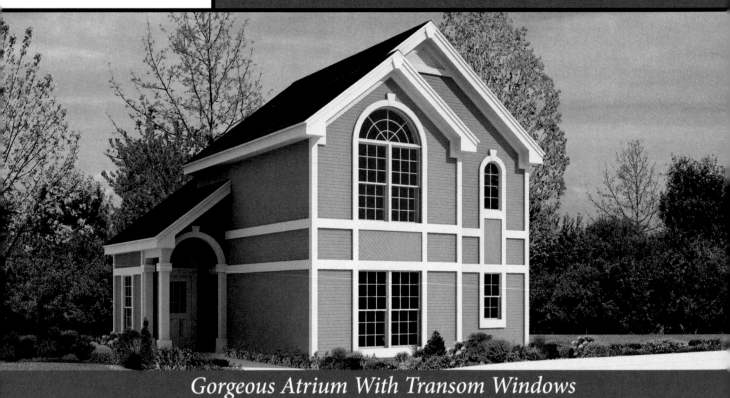

Gorgeous Atrium With Transom Windows

- 902 square feet
- Building height - 27'-4"
- Roof pitch - 9/12
- Ceiling heights:
  First floor - 9'
  Second floor - 8'
- 1 bedroom, 1 bath
- Two 9' x 8' overhead doors
- Large living room connects to an L-shaped kitchen with pantry and dining area/balcony
- Complete list of materials

First Floor

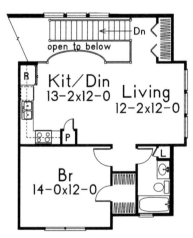

Second Floor

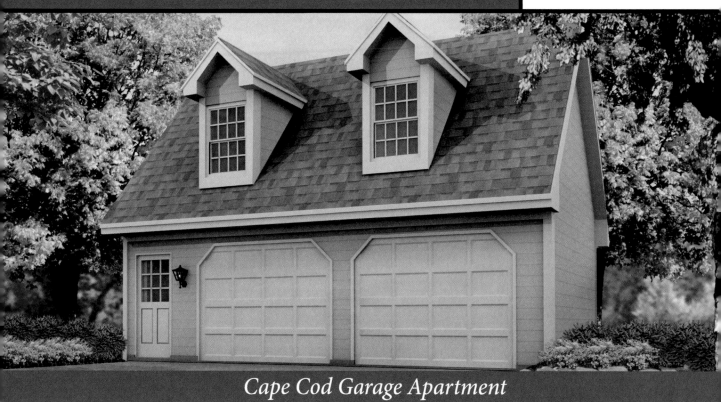

Cape Cod Garage Apartment

- 566 square feet
- Building height - 22'
- Roof pitch - 4.5/12, 12/12
- Ceiling heights:
  First floor - 8'
  Second floor - 7'-7"
- 1 studio area, 1 bath
- Two 9' x 7' overhead doors
- Charming dormers add appeal to this design
- Comfortable open living area
- Complete list of materials
- Step-by-step instructions

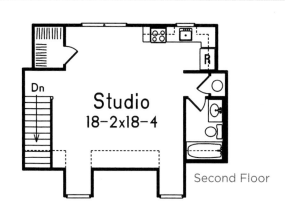

Studio
18-2x18-4

Second Floor

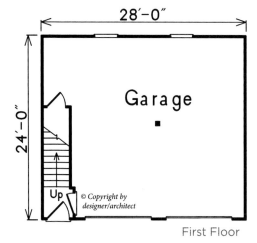

28'-0"

24'-0"

Garage

Up

© Copyright by
designer/architect

First Floor

Spacious Great Room

- 868 square feet
- Building height - 28'
- Roof pitch - 8/12, 10/12
- Ceiling heights:
  First floor - 9'
  Second floor - 8'
- 1 bedroom, 1 bath
- Two 9' x 7' overhead doors
- Large windows brighten the adjoining dining and great rooms
- Complete list of materials

Dining 13x10-4

Kitchen

Great Room 13x11

MBr. 12x10-9

Second Floor

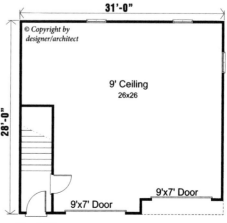

31'-0"

© Copyright by designer/architect

9' Ceiling 26x26

28'-0"

9'x7' Door

9'x7' Door

First Floor

Studio Apartment Garage With Office

- 656 square feet
- Building height - 23'
- Roof pitch - 7/12
- Ceiling heights - 8'
- 1 office/workshop, 1 bath
- 9' x 7' overhead door
- Located behind the garage is the perfect room for an office or workshop and has glass sliding doors to a rear patio
- A well-equipped kitchenette, full bath and a closet/mechanical room are the featured spaces of the efficient studio apartment
- Complete list of materials

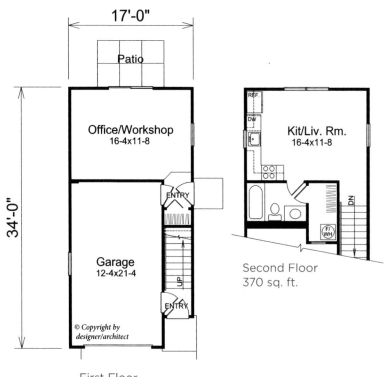

17'-0"

34'-0"

Patio

Office/Workshop
16-4x11-8

ENTRY

Garage
12-4x21-4

© Copyright by
designer/architect

ENTRY

First Floor
286 sq. ft.

REF.

DW

Kit/Liv. Rm.
16-4x11-8

DN

F/
WH

Second Floor
370 sq. ft.

Lovely Front Porch Opens To Shop Area

- 831 square feet
- Building height - 25'-6"
- Roof pitch - 10/12, 10.5/12
- Ceiling heights:
  First floor - 9'
  Second floor - 8'
- 1 bedroom, 1 1/2 baths
- Four 9' x 8' overhead doors
- Shop is 14'-3" x 8'-0" and includes built-in cabinets and toilet room
- Apartment has a living room with rear balcony and kitchen with snack bar and built-in pantry
- Complete list of materials

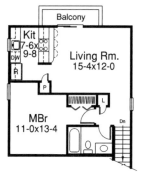

Balcony

Kit
7-6x
9-8

Living Rm.
15-4x12-0

MBr
11-0x13-4

Dn

Second Floor
576 sq. ft.

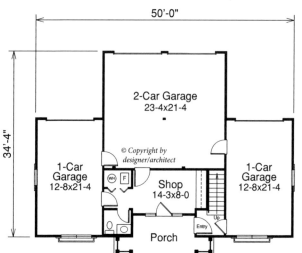

50'-0"

34'-4"

2-Car Garage
23-4x21-4

1-Car Garage
12-8x21-4

© Copyright by designer/architect

Shop
14-3x8-0

1-Car Garage
12-8x21-4

Up

Entry

Porch

First Floor
255 sq. ft.

Cozy Garage Apartment

- 665 square feet
- Building height - 17'
- Roof pitch - 6/12, 8/12
- Ceiling height - 8'
- 1 bedroom, 1 bath
- 16' x 7' overhead door
- Spacious breakfast/sitting area flows into kitchen area
- Complete list of materials

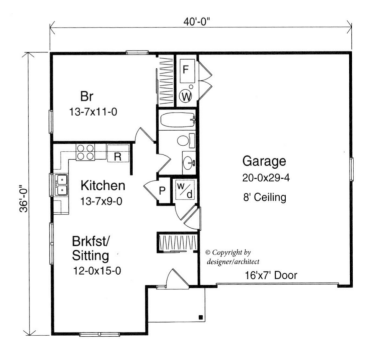

Warming Corner Fireplace

- 588 square feet
- Building height - 16'-6"
- Roof pitch - 7/12, 8/12
- Ceiling height - 8'
- 1 bedroom, 1 bath
- 18' x 7' overhead door
- Living room features a functional entry, bayed dining area, corner fireplace and opens to kitchen with breakfast bar
- Complete list of materials

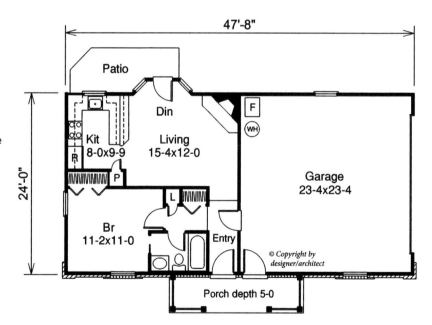

Apartment Garage With Office

- 1,028 square feet
- Building height - 26'-0"
- Roof pitch - 8/12
- Ceiling heights:
  First floor - 8'
  Second floor - 8'
- 1 bedroom, 1 bath
- 16' x 7' overhead door
- Slab foundation
- A vaulted entry with plant shelves and double entry doors guides you to the rear office, an oversized garage and stairs to the second floor living area
- The living room features a vaulted ceiling, fireplace and double patio doors to the front balcony
- Open to the living room is a U-shaped kitchen with snack bar and an ideal dining alcove
- Complete list of materials
- Step-by-step instructions

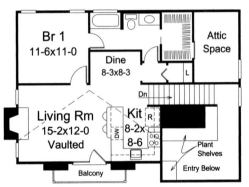

Second Floor
669 sq. ft.

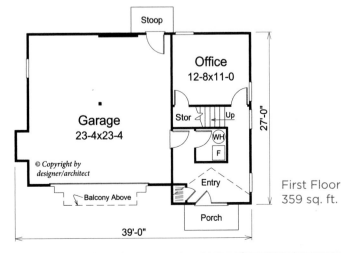

First Floor
359 sq. ft.

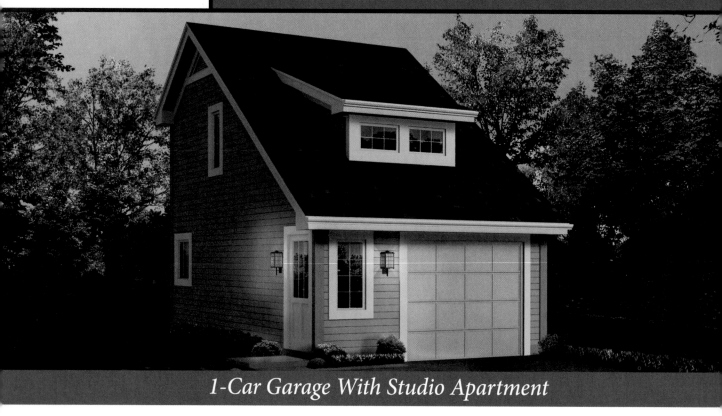

1-Car Garage With Studio Apartment

- 342 square feet
- Building height - 22'-5"
- Roof pitch - 4/12, 8.5/12
- Ceiling heights - 8'
- 1 studio area, 1 bath
- 9' x 7' overhead door
- The first floor consists of a 1-car garage, laundry room, mechanical closet and an entry with door to the outside and stair to second floor
- The second floor features a studio apartment complete with a well-equipped kitchenette alcove, closet and private bath
- Complete list of materials

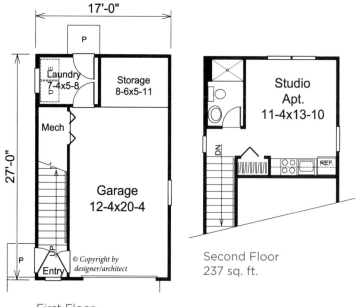

First Floor
105 sq. ft.

Second Floor
237 sq. ft.

© Copyright by designer/architect

Cape Cod Style Garage Apartment

- 813 square feet
- Building height - 22'
- Roof pitch - 4.25/12, 12/12
- Ceiling heights:
  First floor - 8'
  Second floor - 8'
- 1 studio area, 1 bath
- Three 9' x 7' overhead doors
- Spacious studio apartment
  has a kitchen and bath
- Perfect for recreation,
  in-law suite or home office
- Complete list of materials

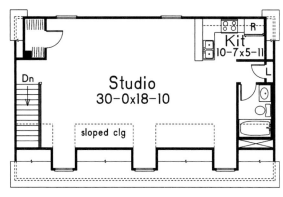

Second Floor

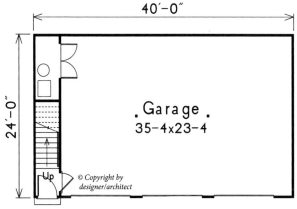

First Floor

Decorative Three-Car Garage Apartment

- 750 square feet
- Building height - 24'-8"
- Roof pitch - 12/12
- Ceiling heights:
  First floor - 8'
  Second floor - 9'
- 1 bedroom, 1 bath
- Three 9' x 7' overhead doors
- The expansive garage features space for a washer/dryer unit and a stairway leading to the spacious apartment
- The eat-in kitchen is designed for efficiency and easily opens to the wide family room
- An optional laundry chute is an exciting addition to add ease to doing the laundry

Second Floor

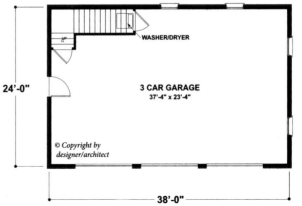

First Floor

Before You Order

Exchange Policies

Since blueprints are printed in response to your order, we cannot honor requests for refunds. However, if for some reason you find that the plan you have purchased does not meet your requirements, you may exchange that plan for another plan in our collection within 90 days of purchase. At the time of the exchange, you will be charged a processing fee of 25% of your original plan package price, plus the difference in price between the plan packages (if applicable) and the cost to ship the new plans to you.

Please note: Reproducible drawings can only be exchanged if the package is unopened. PDF and CAD files are not returnable and non-refundable.

Building Codes & Requirements

At the time the construction drawings were prepared, every effort was made to ensure that these plans and specifications meet nationally recognized codes. Our plans conform to most national building codes. Because building codes vary from area to area, some drawing modifications and/or the assistance of a professional designer or architect may be necessary to comply with your local codes or to accommodate specific building site conditions. We advise you to consult with your local building official for information regarding codes governing your area.

PDF File Format

A complete set of construction drawings in an electronic format that allows you to resize and reproduce the plans to fit your needs. Since these are electronic files, we can send them to you within 24 hours (Mon-Fri, 8-5 CST) via email and save you shipping costs. They also offer printing flexibility by allowing you to print the size and number of sets you need.

Note: These are not CAD files and cannot be altered electronically.

CAD Packages

A CAD package is a complete set of construction drawings in an electronic file format. They are especially beneficial if you have a significant amount of changes to make to the home plan you have selected or if you need to make the home plan fit your local codes. If you purchase a CAD Package, you have the option to take the plan to a local design professional who uses AutoCAD or DataCAD and they can modify the design much easier and quicker than with a paper-based drawing, which will help save you time and money. Just like our reproducible masters, with a CAD package you will receive a one-time build copyright release that allows you to make changes and the necessary copies needed to build your home. For more information and availability, please call our Customer Service Department at 1-877-379-3420.

Garage Plan Index

Apartment Garage Order Form

1.) *Call* toll-free 1-877-379-3420 for credit card orders. Mastercard, Visa, Discover and American Express are accepted.

2.) *Fax* your order to 1-314-770-2226.

3.) *Mail* the Order Form to: *HDA, Inc.*
944 Anglum Road
St. Louis, MO 63042
attn: Customer Service Dept.

4.) *Visit* your Commercial Sales Specialist at your local Lowe's store.

For fastest service, Call Toll-Free 1-877-379-3420 day or night

Order Form

Please send me -

PLAN NUMBER 539-_____

  PRICE CODE_____ (see Plan Page)

Reproducible Masters (call for availability)	$	_____
CAD Package (call for availability)	$	_____
PDF File	$	_____
One-Set of Plans	$	_____
Additional Plan Sets*** (see chart at right)		
_____ (Qty) at _____ $ each	$	_____

SUBTOTAL	$	_____
SALES TAX (MO residents add 7%)	$	_____
☐ Shipping / Handling (see chart at right)	$	_____
(each additional set add $2.00 to shipping charges)		

TOTAL ENCLOSED (US funds only) $ _____

☐ Enclosed is my check or money order
payable to HDA, Inc. (Sorry, no COD's)

I hereby authorize HDA, Inc. to charge this purchase to my credit card account (check one):

☐ MasterCard ☐ VISA ☐ DISCOVER ☐ Cards

Credit Card number _____

Expiration date _____

Signature_____

Name_____
(Please print or type)

Street Address _____
(Please **do not** use PO Box)

City _____

State _____ Zip _____

Daytime phone number (_____) - _____

E-mail _____

Thank you for your order!

Blueprint Price Schedule

Price Code	1-Set	Additional Sets	PDF File/ Reproducible Masters
P12	$250	$30	$300
P13	$310	$45	$610
B	$530	$45	$830

Plan prices are subject to change without notice.
Please note that plans and material lists are not refundable.

Shipping & Handling Charges

	Price Codes P12/P13	Price Code B
U.S. Shipping - (AK & HI express only)		
Regular (allow 7-10 business days)	$5.95	$15.00
Priority (allow 3-5 business days)	$15.00	$35.00
Express* (allow 1-2 business days)	$25.00	$50.00
Canada Shipping (to/from)**		
Standard (allow 8-12 business days)	$15.00	$35.00
Express* (allow 3-5 business days)	$40.00	$75.00

Overseas Shipping/International -
Call, fax, or e-mail (plans@hdainc.com)
for shipping costs.

 * For express delivery please call us
   by 11:00 a.m. Monday-Friday CST
 ** Orders may be subject to custom's fee
   and/or duties/taxes.
 *** An additional set cannot be ordered without the
   purchase of an initial set or reproducible masters

NOTE: Shipping and handling charges do not apply on PDF files.
Orders will be emailed within 24 hours (Mon-Fri., 8-5 CST) of purchase.

Questions? Call Our Customer Service Number
1-877-379-3420

Many of our plans are available in CAD.
For availability, please call our Customer Service Number above.